C000154022

The Supporters' Guide

to

Premier &
Football League
Clubs
2021

EDITOR
Steve Askew

Thirty-seventh Edition

CONTENTS

Foreword 3

Wembley Stadium 4

The F.A. Premier League & the English Football League 5-96

Results for F.A. Premier League 2019/2020 97

Results for the English Football League – The Championship 2019/2020 98

Results for the English Football League – League One 2019/2020 99

Results for the English Football League – League Two 2019/2020 100

Final League Tables & Play-off Results 2019/2020 101-102

F.A. Cup Results 2019/2020 103-105

Football League Cup Results 2019/2020 106-107

England Internationals 2019 to 2020 108-110

The Supporters' Guide Series 111

British Library Cataloguing in Publication Data
A catalogue record for this book is available from the British Library

ISBN: 978-1-86223-428-4

Copyright © 2020, SOCCER BOOKS LIMITED (01472 696226)
72 St. Peter's Avenue, Cleethorpes, N.E. Lincolnshire, DN35 8HU, England
Web site   www.soccer-books.co.uk
e-mail   info@soccer-books.co.uk

All rights are reserved. No part of this publication may be reproduced, stored in a retrieval system or transmitted, in any form or by any means, electronic, mechanical, photocopying, recording, or otherwise, without the prior written permission of Soccer Books Limited.

The Publishers, and the Football Clubs itemised are unable to accept liability for any loss, damage or injury caused by error or inaccuracy in the information published in this guide.

Manufactured in the UK by Severn

FOREWORD

Following the unprecedented effects of the Covid-19 pandemic, the 2019/2020 season in both the F.A. Premier League and the English Football League was suspended on 13th March 2020. The F.A. Premier League resumed play on 17th June and the EFL Championship resumed play on 20th June and the season was completed, albeit with all games played behind closed doors. However, it was already apparent that League One and League Two would not be able to resume play as the expense of the necessary testing and isolation of club staff would be too great, especially with no matchday income. Therefore, on 9th June 2020, the member clubs voted to end the season in these two divisions immediately with league position (and promotion and relegation) calculated on a points per game basis. Play-offs were then held during June and July to decide the final promotion places.

At the time of going to press, it was unclear when fans would again be allowed to attend matches. Quite understandably, therefore, many clubs had not confirmed their admission charges for the coming season. If in doubt, we would suggest contacting clubs before attending games to discover pricing and other relevant requirements.

We are indebted to the staffs of all the clubs featured in this guide for their cooperation and also to Michael Robinson (page layouts), Bob Budd (cover artwork) and Tony Brown (Cup Statistics – www.soccerdata.com).

Disabled Supporters' information is once again included in the guide and, to ensure that facilities are not overstretched, we recommend that fans with disabilities pre-book wherever possible.

Finally, we would like to wish our readers a safe spectating season.

Steve Askew
EDITOR

WEMBLEY STADIUM

First Opened: 1923 (Re-opened in 2007 after rebuild)
Address: Wembley National Stadium, Wembley, London HA9 0WS
Correspondence: P.O.Box 1966, London, SW1P 3EQ
Telephone Nº: 0844 980-8001 or 0800 169-2007
Fax Number: (020) 8795-5050
Stadium Tours: 0800 169-9933

Seating Capacity: 90,000 over three tiers –
  Lower Tier: 34,303 seats
  Middle Tier: 16,532 seats
  Upper Tier: 39,165 seats
Modern Era Record Attendance: 89,874 (2008)
Pitch Size: 115 × 74 yards
Web site: www.wembleystadium.com

GENERAL INFORMATION

Car Parking: The stadium is a Public Transport Location and, as such, parking is only available for pre-accredited vehicles. Any spaces which are available must be pre-purchased from the following web site: www.wembleyofficialparking.com
Coach Travel: National Express operates coach routes from hundreds of towns and cities direct to the stadium for special events: www.nationalexpress.com/wembley
Rail & Tube Travel: Wembley Park station is on the Jubilee and Metropolitan tube lines; Wembley Stadium station is on the Chiltern mainline and Wembley Central station is served by the Bakerloo tube, London Overground and London Midland and Southern railway lines.
Local Bus Services: Services 83, 92, 182 and 223 all travel to the stadium

FANS WITH DISABILITIES INFORMATION

Wheelchairs: 310 spaces for wheelchairs are available in total alongside 310 seats for helpers. A further 100 enhanced amenity seats are available for ambulant visitors. 26 lifts around the stadium assist with access. Wheelchair storage is also available.
Disabled Toilets: 147 toilets are available throughout the stadium with access via the Radar Key system.
Commentary: A 90 minute commentary service is usually available
Contact: For information and assistance contact the Disability liaison officer on 0800 169-2007 (Option 7) or E-mail pod@wembleystadium.com

ACCRINGTON STANLEY FC

Founded: 1876 (Reformed 1968)
Former Names: None
Nickname: 'Stanley' 'Reds'
Ground: Wham Stadium, Livingstone Road,
Accrington, Lancashire BB5 5BX
Record Attendance: 5,387 (26th January 2019)
Pitch Size: 112 × 72 yards

Colours: Red shirts and shorts
Telephone Nº: (01254) 356950
Fax Number: (01254) 356951
Ground Capacity: 5,450
Seating Capacity: 3,100
Web site: www.accringtonstanley.co.uk
E-mail: info@accringtonstanley.co.uk

GENERAL INFORMATION

Car Parking: A limited number of spaces are available at the ground – pre-booking required with a £5.00 charge. Otherwise, street parking only.
Coach Parking: Livingstone Road near the Away entrance
Nearest Railway Station: Accrington (1 mile)
Nearest Bus Station: Accrington Town Centre (1 mile)
Club Shop: At the ground and through the club web site
Opening Times: Weekdays 9.30am – 5.00pm;
Saturday matchdays 10.30am – 5.30pm
Telephone Nº: (01254) 356950

GROUND INFORMATION

Away Supporters' Entrances & Sections:
Coppice Terrave and in the Eric Wallace Stand

ADMISSION INFO (2019/2020 PRICES)

Adult Standing: £20.00   **Adult Seating**: £20.00
Senior Citizen Standing: £15.00
Senior Citizen Seating: £15.00
Ages 12-17 Standing/Seating: £10.00
Under-12s Standing/Seating: £5.00
Programme Price: £3.00

FANS WITH DISABILITIES INFORMATION

Wheelchairs: Specific areas around the ground
Helpers: Admitted
Prices: Normal prices are charged for disabled fans.
One helper is admitted free with each disabled supporter.
Disabled Toilets: Available
Contact: (01254) 356950 or 07754 665730   Robert Houseman, Liaison Officer (Bookings are necessary) –
robert.houseman@accringtonstanley.co.uk

Travelling Supporters' Information:
Routes: Take the M6 to the M65 signposted for Blackburn/Burnley. Exit at Junction 7 and follow the sign for Padiham. Turn right at first traffic lights then right at next. Follow Whalley Road towards Accrington, go through lights at the Greyhound Inn. Turn left into Livingstone Road, 500 yards past traffic lights (signposted Accrington Stanley). The ground is signposted from Junction 7 of the M65 – follow the brown signs with the white football.

AFC BOURNEMOUTH

Founded: 1899 (**Entered League**: 1923)
Former Names: Boscombe FC (1899-1923);
Bournemouth & Boscombe Athletic FC (1923-1972)
Nickname: 'Cherries'
Ground: Vitality Stadium, Dean Court,
Bournemouth, Dorset   BH7 7AF
Ground Capacity: 11,364 (All seats)

Record Attendance: 11,772 (21st July 2013)
Pitch Size: 115 × 74 yards
Colours: Red & Black striped shirts with Black shorts
Telephone Nº & Ticket Office Nº: 0344 576-1910
Fax Number: (01202) 726373
Web Site: www.afcb.co.uk
E-mail: enquiries@afcb.co.uk

GENERAL INFORMATION

Car Parking: Car Park for 200 cars behind the ground and free parking is available at Harewood College (10 mins. walk)
Coach Parking: At the ground
Nearest Railway Station: Bournemouth Central (1½ miles)
Nearest Bus Stop: Holdenhurst Road, Bournemouth
Club Shop: At the ground
Opening Times: Monday to Friday 9.00am to 5.00pm, Saturday 9.30am to 4.00pm, Sunday 10.00am to 3.00pm and Saturday Matchdays 9.00am to kick-off + 30 minutes after the final whistle.
Telephone Nº: 0844 576 -1910

GROUND INFORMATION

Away Supporters' Entrances & Sections:
East Stand turnstiles 'F' 14-16 for East Stand accommodation

ADMISSION INFO (2019/2020 PRICES)

Adult Seating: £32.00 – £55.00
Child Seating: £6.00 – £18.00
Concessionary Seating: £19.00 – £40.00
Note: Family tickets are also available. In view of the limited capacity of Dean Court, most seats for 2019/2020 will be taken by season ticket holders.

FANS WITH DISABILITIES INFORMATION

Wheelchairs: Spaces available in all stands
Helpers: One carer admitted per fan with disabilities
Prices: £5.00 for those in wheelchairs.
Disabled Toilets: Available in Main, East and North Stands
Contact: (01202) 726311 Alice Jeans   (Bookings are necessary)
E-mail Contact: disability@afcb.co.uk

Travelling Supporters' Information: Routes: From the North & East: Take the A338 into Bournemouth and turn left at 'Kings Park' turning. After the slip road go straight forward at the mini-roundabout into Kings Park Drive – a car park is 500 yards on the left and the ground is nearby; From the West: Head into Bournemouth and join the A338, take the slip road at the Springbourne Roundabout, signposted for Kings Park. Take the 3rd exit at the roundabout at the fire station, stay in the left-hand lane and turn left onto Holdenhurst Road. Go straight on at the traffic lights (the Queen's Park Pub should be on the right) and take the 3rd exit at the mini roundabout into Kings Park for the ground.

AFC WIMBLEDON

AFC Wimbledon are in the process of moving to a new stadium being built close to their former home, Plough Lane. It was originally hoped that the new stadium would be open towards the end of October 2020 though it remains to be seen if the pandemic will affect these plans. The club are playing their home games at QPR's ground (see page 72) until the new stadium is open. At the time of going to press, little information was available about the new stadium so we suggest contacting the club directly for more details. The image above shows their most recent home, Kingsmeadow.

Founded: 2002 (**Entered League**: 2011)
Former Names: Originally formed as Wimbledon Old Centrals (1889-1905) who later became Wimbledon FC
Nickname: 'The Dons'
Ground: New Plough Lane, Wimbledon   SW17 0BL
Record Attendance: 4,870 (2016 – King's Meadow)

Ground Capacity: 9,300 (All seats)
Colours: Shirts and Shorts are Blue with Yellow trim
Telephone Nº: (020) 8547-3528 (Office hours only)
Fax Number: 0808 280-0816
Web site: www.afcwimbledon.co.uk
E-mail: info@afcwimbledon.co.uk

GENERAL INFORMATION

Car Parking: Please contact the club for information
Coach Parking: Please contact the club for information
Nearest Railway Station: Haydon's Road (½ mile)
Nearest Tube Station: Tooting Broadway/Wimbledon Park (both 1 mile)
Club Shop: Please contact the club for information
Opening Times: –
Telephone Nº: (020) 8547-3528

GROUND INFORMATION

Away Supporters' Entrances & Sections:
Please contact the club for information

ADMISSION INFO (2020/2021 PRICES)

Adult Seating: £22.00 – £32.00
Concessionary Seating: £15.00 – £22.00
Under-22s Seating: £11.00 – £16.00
Under-18s Seating: £6.00 – £11.00
Under-12s Seating: £3.00 – £5.00

FANS WITH DISABILITIES INFORMATION

Wheelchairs: Please contact the club for information
Helpers: Admitted
Prices: Please contact the club for information
Disabled Toilets: Available
Contact: (020) 8547-3528 (Bookings are necessary)

Travelling Supporters' Information:
Routes: The new stadium is being constructed on the site of the former Wimbledon Greyhound Stadium. Please contact the club for directions.

ARSENAL FC

Founded: 1886 (**Entered League**: 1893)
Former Names: Royal Arsenal (1886-1891) and Woolwich Arsenal (1891-1914)
Nickname: 'Gunners'
Ground: Emirates Stadium, Hornsey Road, London, N7 7AJ
Ground Capacity: 60,260 (All seats)
Pitch Size: 115 × 74 yards
Record Attendance: 60,161 (3rd November 2007)

Colours: Red shirts with White sleeves, White shorts
Telephone Nº: (020) 7619-5003
Ticket Office: (020) 7619-5000
Fax Number: (020) 7704-4001
Office Address: Highbury House, 75 Drayton Park, London N5 1BU
Web Site: www.arsenal.com
E-mail: ask@arsenal.co.uk

GENERAL INFORMATION

Car Parking: None
Coach Parking: Visit the web site for further details
Nearest Railway Station: Finsbury Park and Highbury & Islington
Nearest Tube Station: Arsenal (Piccadilly), Finsbury Park, Highbury & Islington and Holloway Road are all nearby
Club Shop: At the ground and at Finsbury Park Tube Station
Opening Times: Monday to Saturday 9.00am to 6.00pm; Sundays 10.00am to 4.00pm (9.00am to 6.00pm at Finsbury Park)
Telephone Nº: (020) 7619-5000

GROUND INFORMATION

Away Supporters' Entrances & Sections:
Green quadrant in the south east corner of the ground – follow colour coding system at the ground

ADMISSION INFO (2020/2021 PRICES)

Adult Seating: £27.00 – £97.00
Child Seating: £10.00 – £32.50 (Members only)
Senior Citizen Seating: £11.25 – £36.50 (Members only)
Note: Prices vary depending on the category of the game. Concessionary prices are only available to Members.
Programme Price: £3.00

FANS WITH DISABILITIES INFORMATION

Wheelchairs: 250 spaces available in areas throughout the ground. A similar number of places are available for the ambulant and visually impaired
Helpers: One helper admitted for each fan with disabilities
Prices: £13.25 – £46.00. Helpers are admitted free
Disabled Toilets: Many available throughout the ground
Free commentaries are available for the visually impaired
Contact: (020) 7619-5050 (Bookings are necessary) – Alun Francis (DAO) – E-mail afrancis@arsenal.co.uk or disability@arsenal.co.uk

Travelling Supporters' Information:
As the stadium is situated in a mainly residential area, only car owners with resident's permits will be allowed to park in the designated on-street parking areas. Cars parked illegally will be towed away so use public transport whenever possible. The nearest tube station is Arsenal (Piccadilly Line) which is 3 minutes walk from the ground with Finsbury Park (Victoria & Piccadilly Lines) and Highbury & Islington about 10 minutes walk away.

ASTON VILLA FC

Photo courtesy of Neville Williams/Aston Villa FC

Founded: 1874 **(Entered League**: 1888)
Former Names: None
Nicknames: 'The Villans' 'Villa'
Ground: Villa Park, Trinity Road, Birmingham B6 6HE
Ground Capacity: 42,095 (All seats)
Record Attendance: 76,588 (2nd March 1946)
Pitch Size: 115 × 75 yards

Colours: Claret shirts with Blue sleeves, White shorts
Telephone Nº: (0121) 327-2299
Fax Number: (0121) 322-2107
Ticket Office: 0333 323-1874
Consumer Sales: 0330 053-6010
Web Site: www.avfc.co.uk
E-mail: postmaster@avfc.co.uk

GENERAL INFORMATION

Ground Tours: 0333 323-1874
Car Parking: Stadium Car Park (permit only on matchdays) or street parking away from the ground
Away Coach Parking: Opposite the ground on Witton Lane
Nearest Railway Station: Witton or Aston (5 mins. walk)
Nearest Bus Station: Birmingham Centre
Club Shop: 'Villa Village' at the ground
Opening Times: Villa Village: Monday to Saturday 10.00am to 5.00pm (9.00am on Saturday) & Sunday 10.00am to 4.00pm.
Telephone Nº: 0330 053-6010

GROUND INFORMATION

Away Supporters' Entrances & Sections:
Doug Ellis Stand – Blocks 'P' & 'Q'

ADMISSION INFO (2020/2021 PRICES)

Adult Seating: £20.00 – £50.00
Concessionary Seating: £15.00 – £32.00
Under-21s Seating: £10.00 – £20.00
Under-18s Seating: £5.00 – £14.00
Under-14s Seating: £5.00 – £14.00 (must be accompanied by a paying adult
Programme Price: £3.50

FANS WITH DISABILITIES INFORMATION

Wheelchairs: 87 spaces in total in the Trinity Road Stand lower, 8 of which are for away supporters
Helpers: Admitted on request – one per fan with disabilities
Prices: Concessionary prices for fans with disabilities
Disabled Toilets: Available in the Trinity Road Stand lower
Contact: 0800 612-0970 ext. 344 (Bookings are necessary)
E-mail contact: disability@avfc.co.uk – Sheila Maybury (DAO) (0121) 327-2299 extension 344

Travelling Supporters' Information: From all parts: Exit M6 at Junction 6 (Spaghetti Junction). Follow signs for Birmingham (NE). Take the 4th exit at the roundabout onto the A38 (M) signposted Aston. After ½ mile, turn right into Aston Hall Road.
Bus Services: Service 7 from Colmore Circus to Witton Square. Also some specials.

BARNSLEY FC

Founded: 1887 (**Entered League**: 1898)
Former Names: Barnsley St. Peter's
Nickname: 'The Tykes' 'Reds'
Ground: Oakwell Stadium, Barnsley   S71 1ET
Ground Capacity: 23,287 (All seats)
Record Attendance: 40,255 (15th February 1936)
Pitch Size: 110 × 75 yards

Colours: Red shirts with White shorts and Red socks
Telephone Nº: (01226) 211211
Ticket Office: (01226) 211183
Fax Number: (01226) 211444
Web Site: www.barnsleyfc.co.uk
E-mail: thereds@barnsleyfc.co.uk

GENERAL INFORMATION

Car Parking: Queen's Ground Car Park (adjacent)
Coach Parking: Queen's Ground Car Park
Nearest Railway Station: Barnsley Interchange (6 minutes walk)
Nearest Bus Station: Barnsley Interchange
Club Shop: At the Stadium
Opening Times: Please contact the club for details due to uncertainty caused by the pandemic.
Telephone Nº: (01226) 211400

GROUND INFORMATION

Away Supporters' Entrances & Sections:
Palmer Construction North Stand Turnstiles 42-51

ADMISSION INFO (2019/2020 PRICES)

Adult Seating: £23.00 – £36.00
Concessionary Seating: £16.00 – £28.00
Under-19s Seating: £10.00
Under-12s Seating: £5.00
Note: Prices are lower for tickets purchased in advance
Programme Price: £3.00

FANS WITH DISABILITIES INFORMATION

Wheelchairs: 60 wheelchair spaces available in total in designated disabled areas including 18 spaces for Away fans in the North Stand.
Helpers: Admitted
Prices: Normal prices for fans with disabilities but helpers are admitted free of charge
Disabled Toilets: Available in the Corner Stand, North Stand and C.K. Beckett Stand
Commentaries are available for the blind
Contact: (01266) 211183   (Bookings are necessary) – Vicky Campbell (Disability Liaison Officer)

Travelling Supporters' Information: From All Parts: Exit the M1 at Junction 37 and follow the 'Barnsley FC/Football Ground' signs which lead to a large surface car park adjacent to the stadium (2 miles).

BARROW AFC

Founded: 1901 (**Re-entered League**: 2020)
Former Names: None
Nickname: 'Bluebirds'
Ground: The Progression Solicitors Stadium, Wilkie Road, Barrow-in-Furness   LA14 5UW
Record Attendance: 16,874 (vs Swansea City, 1954)
Pitch Size: 110 × 75 yards

Colours: White shirts with Blue sleeves, Blue shorts
Telephone Nº: (01229) 666010
Ground Capacity: 5,045
Seating Capacity: 1,000
Web site: www.barrowafc.com
E-mail: office@barrowafc.com

GENERAL INFORMATION
Car Parking: Street Parking, Popular Side Car Park and Soccer Bar Car Park
Coach Parking: Adjacent to the ground
Nearest Railway Station: Barrow Central (½ mile)
Nearest Bus Station: ½ mile (Bus No. 3 stops at the ground)
Club Shop: At the ground
Opening Times: Monday to Friday 9.00am to 4.00pm and Saturday Home Matchdays 12.00pm to 2.55pm.
Telephone Nº: (01229) 666010

GROUND INFORMATION
Away Supporters' Entrances & Sections:
Holker Street End (uncovered terrace)

ADMISSION INFO (2020/2021 PRICES)
Adult Standing: £16.00
Adult Seating: £19.00
Concessionary Standing: £13.00
Concessionary Seating: £15.00
Under-18s Standing/Seating: £5.00
Under-18s Standing/Seating: £6.00

DISABLED INFORMATION
Wheelchairs: 6 spaces available in the Disabled Area
Helpers: Admitted
Prices: Normal prices apply
Disabled Toilets: Available
Contact: (01229) 666010   (Bookings are not necessary) – Robert Graham (Disability Liaison Officer)

Travelling Supporters' Information:
Routes: Exit the M6 at Junction 36 and take the A590 through Ulverston. Using the bypass, follow signs for Barrow. After approximately 5 miles, turn left into Wilkie Road and the ground is on the right.

BIRMINGHAM CITY FC

Founded: 1875 (**Entered League**: 1892)
Former Names: Small Heath Alliance FC (1875-88);
Small Heath FC (1888-1905); Birmingham FC (1905-45)
Nickname: 'The Blues'
Ground: St. Andrew's Trillion Trophy Stadium,
Birmingham   B9 4RL
Ground Capacity: 29,409 (All seats)
Record Attendance: 68,844 (11th March 1939)

Pitch Size: 109 × 74 yards
Colours: Shirts are Royal Blue with White sleeves,
White shorts
Telephone N°: (0121) 772-0101
Ticket Office: (0121) 772-0101 (Option 2)
Web Site: www.bcfc.com
E-mail: reception@bcfc.com

GENERAL INFORMATION

Car Parking: Street Parking + Birmingham Wheels (secure parking but not related to the club)
Coach Parking: Coventry Road
Nearest Railway Station: Birmingham New Street or Birmingham Moor Street (20 minutes walk)
Nearest Bus Station: Digbeth National Express Coach Station
Club Shops: Blues Store at the ground
Opening Times: Monday to Saturday 9.00am to 5.00pm. Matchdays open from 9.00am until kick-off then for a further 30 minutes after the game. Sundays 10.30am to 4.30pm.
Telephone N°: (0121) 772-0101 (Option 4)

GROUND INFORMATION

Away Supporters' Entrances & Sections:
Gil Merrick Stand, Coventry Road

ADMISSION INFO (2019/2020 PRICES)

Adult Seating: £15.00 – £35.00
Under-19s Seating: £10.00 – £25.00
Under-13s Seating: £5.00 – £20.00
Concessionary Seating: £10.00 – £30.00
Note: Prices vary depending on the category of the match and the location of the seat.

FANS WITH DISABILITIES INFORMATION

Wheelchairs: 88 spaces in total (including 21 for Away fans) in the Spion Kop Stand, Gil Merrick Lower Stand, Tilton Road Stand and East Paddocks
Helpers: One assistant admitted for each fan with disabilities
Prices: Normal prices apply for fans with disabilities. Helpers are admitted free of charge
Disabled Toilets: 14 available in the Spion Kop Stand, Family Stand, Gil Merrick Stand and Tilton Road Stand
Contact: (0121) 772-0101 Option 2 (Bookings are necessary)
Aamir Javaid (Dsability Co-ordinator) – aamir.javaid@bcfc.com

Travelling Supporters' Information: From All Parts: Exit M6 at Junction 6 and take the A38 (M) (Aston Expressway). Leave at 2nd exit then take first exit at roundabout along the Dartmouth Middleway. After 1¼ miles turn left on to Coventry Road.
Bus Services: Services 17, 58, 59 & 60 from Birmingham Centre stop at Cattell Road just to the south of the stadium and Services 97f stops at Garrison Lane just to the north of the stadium.

BLACKBURN ROVERS FC

Founded: 1875 (**Entered League**: 1888)
Nickname: 'Rovers' 'Blues & Whites'
Ground: Ewood Park, Blackburn,
Lancashire   BB2 4JF
Pitch Size: 115 × 72 yards
Ground Capacity: 31,367 (All seats)
Record Attendance: 62,255 vs Bolton (2/3/1929)

Colours: Blue and White halved shirts, White shorts
Telephone Nº: (01254) 372001
Ticket Office: (01254) 372000
Fax Number: (01254) 671042
Web Site: www.rovers.co.uk
Contact E-mail: enquiries@rovers.co.uk

GENERAL INFORMATION

Car Parking: 800 spaces available at the ground
Coach Parking: At the ground (Darwen End)
Nearest Railway Station: Blackburn Central (1½ miles)
Nearest Bus Station: Blackburn Central (1½ miles)
Club Shop: Roverstore at the ground
Opening Times: Weekdays 9.00am – 5.00pm, Saturday
10.00am–3.00pm, closed on Sundays.
Telephone Nº: (01254) 508137 (Ewood shop)

GROUND INFORMATION

Away Supporters' Entrances & Sections:
Darwen End

ADMISSION INFO (2019/2020 PRICES)

Adult Seating: £22.00 – £45.00
Senior Citizen Seating: £15.00 – £35.00
Under-26s Seating: £10.00 – £30.00
Under-18s Seating: £7.00 – £16.00
Under-12s Seating: £5.00 – £14.00
Programme Price: £3.00

FANS WITH DISABILITIES INFORMATION

Wheelchairs: 262 spaces for Home fans and 30 for Away fans
Helpers: One helper admitted per fan with disabilities.
Applications for helpers tickets must be made in advance
Prices: Normal prices apply for both fans with disabilities
and their helpers
Disabled Toilets: 14 purpose-built ground level toilets
Commentaries available via Radio Rovers – bring a radio!
Contact: 0771 772-4646   **E-mail**: disability@rovers.co.uk
Christine Rennard MBE (DLO) – (01254) 508205

Travelling Supporters' Information: Routes: Supporters travelling Northbound on the M6: Exit the M6 at Junction 29, follow the M65 and exit at Junction 4 for Ewood Park. The ground is ¾ mile from Junction 4 – please look for parking areas to avoid congestion around the ground; Supporters travelling Northbound on the M61: Exit the M61 at Junction 9, join the M65 and exit at Junction 4 (then as above); Supporters travelling Southbound on the M6: Exit the M6 at Junction 30, follow the M61 and exit at Junction 9 onto the M65. Exit the M65 at Junction 4 for the ground; Supporters from the Yorkshire Area either on the B6234, the A56 Haslingden by-pass or the A59 Skipton Road – please follow signs for Ewood Park (follow Preston M65 and exit at Junction 4).

BLACKPOOL FC

Founded: 1887 **(Entered League**: 1896)
Former Name: Merged with Blackpool St. Johns (1887)
Nickname: 'Seasiders' or 'Tangerines'
Ground: Bloomfield Road, Blackpool, FY1 6JJ
Ground Capacity: 16,616 (All seats)
Record Attendance: 38,098 (17th September 1955)
Pitch Size: 112 × 75 yards

Colours: Tangerine shirts with White shorts
Telephone Nº: (01253) 599344
Ticket Office: (01253) 599745
Web Site: www.blackpoolfc.co.uk
E-mail: tickets@blackpoolfc.co.uk

GENERAL INFORMATION

Car Parking: 3,000 spaces at the ground and street parking
Coach Parking: Available at the ground
Nearest Railway Station: Blackpool South (5 mins. walk)
Nearest Bus Station: Talbot Road (2 miles)
Club Shop: At the ground
Opening Times: Weekdays 9.00am to 5.00pm (until kick-off on Tuesday matchdays). Saturdays 9.00am to 12.00pm but until kick-off and for 30 minutes after the game on Saturday matchdays.
Telephone Nº: (01253) 599745

GROUND INFORMATION

Away Supporters' Entrances & Sections:
North Side entrances for the East Stand (temporary)

ADMISSION INFO (2020/2021 PRICES)

Adult Seating: £19.00 – £28.00
Senior Citizen/Age 17 to 21 Seating: £17.00 – £26.00
Under-17s Seating: £9.00 – £15.00
Under-12s Seating: £4.00 – £10.00
Under-5s Seating: £5.00 (free in some areas. Must be accompanied by a paying adult).
Programme Price: £3.00

FANS WITH DISABILITIES INFORMATION

Wheelchairs: Over 50 spaces in total for home and away fans
Helpers: One helper admitted with each fan with disabilities
Prices: Normal prices apply
Disabled Toilets: Available
Contact: 07875 236576 (Bookings are necessary) – Chris Beveridge – chris.beveridge@blackpoolfc.co.uk

Travelling Supporters' Information: From All Parts: Exit M6 at Junction 32 onto the M55. Follow signs for the main car parks along the new 'spine' road to the car parks at the side of the ground.

BOLTON WANDERERS FC

Founded: 1874 (**Entered League:** 1888)
Former Names: Christchurch FC (1874-1877)
Nickname: 'Trotters'
Ground: University of Bolton Stadium, Burnden Way, Lostock, Bolton, Lancashire   BL6 6JW
Ground Capacity: 28,723 (All seats)
Pitch Size: 115 × 75 yards

Record Attendance: 28,353 (vs Leicester City, 2003)
Colours: White shirts with Navy Blue shorts
Telephone Nº: (01204) 673673
Ticket Office: 0844 871-2932
Fax Number: (01204) 673773
Web Site: www.bwfc.co.uk
E-mail: reception@bwfc.co.uk

GENERAL INFORMATION

Car Parking: 2,800 spaces available at the ground (£7.00)
Coach Parking: Available at the ground (£20.00)
Nearest Railway Station: Horwich Parkway (600 yards)
Nearest Bus Station: Moor Lane, Bolton
Club Shop: At the ground
Opening Times: Daily from 9.30am to 5.30pm
Telephone Nº: (01204) 673650

GROUND INFORMATION

Away Supporters' Entrances & Sections:
South Stand entrances and accommodation

ADMISSION INFO (2018/2019 PRICES)

Adult Seating: £15.00 – £35.00
Concessionary Seating: £10.00 – £29.00
Under-18s Seating: £10.00 – £12.00
Under-12s Seating: £10.00
Note: Prices vary depending on the grading of the game. Prices for the 2019/2020 season were not available at the time of going to press. Please contact the club for information.

FANS WITH DISABILITIES INFORMATION

Wheelchairs: 32 spaces available for visiting fans, 72 spaces for home fans
Helpers: One helper admitted free with each disabled fan
Prices: Normal prices apply for fans with disabilities
Disabled Toilets: Available
Contact: (01204) 673652 (Bookings are necessary)
Daniel Scott (DLO) – dscott@bwfc.co.uk

Travelling Supporters' Information:
From All Parts: Exit the M61 at Junction 6 and the ground is clearly visible ¼ mile away.

BRADFORD CITY FC

Founded: 1903 (**Entered League**: 1903)
Nickname: 'Bantams'
Ground: The Utilita Energy Stadium, Valley Parade, Bradford   BD8 7DY
Ground Capacity: 24,840 (All seats)
Record Attendance: 39,146 (11th March 1911)
Pitch Size: 113 × 70 yards

Colours: Claret and Amber Striped shirts with Black shorts and socks
Telephone Nº: (01274) 773355
Ticket Office: (01274) 770012
Fax Number: (01274) 773356
Web Site: www.bradfordcityfc.co.uk
E-mail: support@bradfordcityfc.co.uk

GENERAL INFORMATION

Car Parking: Street Parking and Car Parks (£3.00 charge)
Coach Parking: By Police direction
Nearest Railway Station: Bradford Foster Square
Nearest Bus Station: Bradford Interchange (1 mile)
Club Shop: At the ground
Opening Times: Monday to Friday 9.30am to 5.00pm and Saturday 10.00am to 3.00pm
Telephone Nº: (01274) 734521
Shop Web Site: www.bantams.clubstore.co.uk

GROUND INFORMATION

Away Supporters' Entrances & Sections:
Blocks F and G in the Mamma Mia (East) Stand (entrances on Midland Road)

ADMISSION INFO (2019/2020 PRICES)

Adult Seating: £25.00 (£20.00 purchased in advance)
Under-16s Seating: £10.00
Senior Citizen/Student Seating: £15.00
Note: Under-11s are admitted for £5.00 when accompanied by a paying adult – up to 3 Under-11s admitted per adult.
Programme Price: £3.00

FANS WITH DISABILITIES INFORMATION

Wheelchairs: 100 spaces available in total for Home and Away fans throughout the ground. Access for away supporters is in the South Stand
Helpers: One helper admitted per fan with disabilities
Prices: Normal prices for fans with disabilities. Helpers free
Disabled Toilets: Available in all stands
Contact: 07818 515639 (Bookings are necessary)
Jamie Dorward (DLO) – jamiedorward@bradfordcityfc.co.uk

Travelling Supporters' Information: Routes: Exit the M62 at Junction 26 and take the M606 towards Bradford. At the end of the motorway get in the middle lane and follow signs for Bradford (West) into Rooley Lane (signs for the Airport). A McDonalds is now on your left. Turn left into Wakefield Road at the roundabout and stay in the middle lane. Continue straight on over two roundabouts (signs to Shipley and Skipton) onto Shipley Airedale Road which then becomes Canal Road. Just after Tesco on the left, turn left into Station Road and left again into Queens Road. Go up the hill to the third set of traffic lights and turn left into Manningham Lane. After the Gulf petrol station on the left, turn first left into Valley Parade for the Stadium.

BRENTFORD FC

> No photograph of the new stadium was available at the time of going to press.

Founded: 1889 (**Entered League**: 1920)
Nickname: 'The Bees'
Ground: Brentford Community Stadium, 166 Lionel Road North, Brentford TW8 9QT
Ground Capacity: 17,250 (All seats)
Record Attendance: 38,678 (26th February 1949)

Pitch Size: 114 × 74 yards
Colours: Red & White striped shirts with Black shorts
Telephone Nº: (020) 8847-2511
Ticket Office: 0333 005-8521
Web Site: www.brentfordfc.com
E-mail: enquiries@brentfordfc.com

GENERAL INFORMATION

Car Parking: Street Parking only. It is recommended that fans do not travel to the Stadium by car but instead use the many nearby public transport links.
Coach Parking: By Police direction
Nearest Railway Station: Kew Bridge (100 metres)
Nearest Tube Station: Gunnersbury (¾ mile)
Bus Routes: Numbers N9, 65, 237, 267 & 391 pass the ground.
Club Shop: At the ground
Opening Times: Weekdays 10.00am–4.00pm and Saturday Matchdays 12.00pm until kick-off and then for one hour after the game.
Telephone Nº: (020) 8847-2511 Option 4

GROUND INFORMATION

Away Supporters' Entrances & Sections:
North east corner

ADMISSION INFO (2019/2020 PRICES)

Adult Standing: £23.00 – £25.00
Adult Seating: £23.00 – £30.00
Under-18s Standing/Seating: £6.00 – £8.00
Senior Citizen Standing: £17.00 – £19.00
Senior Citizen Seating: £17.00 – £24.00
Ages 18 to 24 Standing: £15.00 – £17.00
Ages 18 to 24 Seating: £15.00 – £22.00
Programme Price: £3.00

FANS WITH DISABILITIES INFORMATION

Wheelchairs: 50 spaces available in total in the West, South and East Stands
Helpers: One helper admitted per fan with disabilities
Prices: Normal prices for fans with disabilities. Helpers free
Disabled Toilets: Available throughout the ground
Contact: (020) 8847-2511 Option 1 (Bookings necessary) Ashley Cheatley – ashley@brentfordfc.com

Travelling Supporters' Information: The stadium is situated just to the south of the M4 and just 100 metres from Kew Bridge station. It is recommended that fans do not travel to the Stadium by car but instead use the many nearby public transport links. In addition to Kew Bridge, the stadium is situated within 1 mile of railway stations at Brentford, Gunnersbury and Kew Gardens and London Underground stations at Acton Town, Gunnersbury and Chiswick Park.

BRIGHTON & HOVE ALBION FC

Founded: 1901 (**Entered League**: 1920)
Nickname: 'Seagulls'
Ground: American Express Community Stadium, Village Way, Brighton BN1 9BL
Ground Capacity: 30,750 (All seats)
Pitch Size: 115 × 75 yards
Record Attendance: 30,682 (vs Liverpool, 2019)

Colours: Blue & White striped shirts with Blue shorts
Telephone Nº: (01273) 668855
Ticket Office: (01273) 668855 Option 1
Fax Number: (01273) 878238
Web Site: www.brightonandhovealbion.com
E-mail: supporter.services@brightonandhovealbion.com

GENERAL INFORMATION

Car Parking: Limited parking at the stadium and 700 spaces available at the University campus (adjacent)
Coach Parking: At the stadium
Nearest Railway Station: Falmer (adjacent)
Nearest Bus Station: Brighton
Club Shop: At the stadium
Opening Times: Monday to Saturday 9.30am to 5.00pm and Sundays 11.00am to 4.00pm. Saturday Matchdays open 9.00am to kick-off then after the game until either 6.00pm or 10.30pm, depending on kick-off time.
Telephone Nº: (01273) 668855 Option 3

GROUND INFORMATION

Away Supporters' Entrances & Sections:
South Stand

ADMISSION INFO (2019/2020 PRICES)

Adult Seating: £30.00 – £65.00
Under-18s Seating: £15.00 – £32.00
Under-21s/Senior Citizen Seating: £23.00 – £45.00
Note: Prices vary depending on the category of the game. It is anticipated that Photo ID and use of a Track and Trace may be required for entry to the ground.
Programme Price: £3.50

FANS WITH DISABILITIES INFORMATION

Wheelchairs: 185 spaces available in total
Helpers: One helper admitted per fan with disabilities
Prices: Normal prices for fans with disabilities. Helpers free
Disabled Toilets: Yes – in all the stands
Contact: (01273) 668855 Opt 1   (Bookings are necessary) Millie Crowhurst (Disability Liaison Officer)

Travelling Supporters' Information: Routes: From the North: Take the M23 then the A23 to Brighton. At the roundabout on the outskirts of Brighton, take the exit onto the A27 towards Lewes. Pass the A270 turn-off and continue towards the village of Falmer. The stadium is situated by the side of the A27 in the village of Falmer across the road from the University of Sussex campus; From the East and West: Take the A27 to Falmer which is located to the north-east of Brighton. Then as above.

BRISTOL CITY FC

Founded: 1894 (**Entered League**: 1901)
Former Name: Bristol South End FC (1894-1897)
Nickname: 'The Robins'
Ground: Ashton Gate Stadium, Bristol   BS3 2EJ
Ground Capacity: 27,000 (All seats)
Pitch Size: 115 × 75 yards
Record Attendance: 43,335 (16th February 1935)

Colours: Red shirts with White shorts
Telephone Nº: (0117) 963-0600
Ticket Hotline: (0117) 963-0600 (Option 1)
Fax Number: (0117) 963-0700
Web Site: www.bcfc.co.uk
E-mail: supporterservices@bristol-sport.co.uk

GENERAL INFORMATION

Car Parking: Street parking and also at Bedminster Cricket Club (5 minutes walk)
Coach Parking: By prior arrangement with the club
Nearest Railway Station: Bristol Temple Meads (1½ miles)
Nearest Bus Station: Bristol City Centre
Club Shop: BCFC Megastore at the ground
Opening Times: Monday to Saturday 9.00am to 5.00pm and weekend matchdays from 5.00pm until half an hour after the final whistle.
Telephone Nº: (0117) 963-0600 (Option 0 then Option 1)

GROUND INFORMATION

Away Supporters' Entrances & Sections:
Atyeo Stand – Turnstiles 39-46 via Ashton Road

ADMISSION INFO (2019/2020 PRICES)

Adult Seating: £25.00 – £42.00
Under-25s/Senior Citizen Seating: £22.00 – £39.00
Under-22s Seating: £19.00 – £36.00
Under-19s Seating: £15.00 – £23.00
Under-12s Seating: £10.00 – £18.00
Note: A membership scheme offers discounted prices for advance bookings. Prices vary depending on game category
Programme Price: £3.00

FANS WITH DISABILITIES INFORMATION

Wheelchairs: 20 spaces are available for away fans
Helpers: One helper admitted per fan with disabilities
Prices: Normal prices for fans with disabilities. Helpers free
Disabled Toilets: Available in various areas of the ground
Commentaries are available for the blind
Contact: (0117) 963-0600 Option 1 (Bookings are necessary)
Gareth Torpey – gareth.torpey@bristol-sport.co.uk

Travelling Supporters' Information: Routes: From the North & West: Exit the M5 at Junction 16, take the A38 to Bristol City Centre and follow the A38 Taunton signs. Cross the swing bridge after 1¼ miles and bear left into Winterstoke Road for the ground; From the East: Take the M4 then M32 and follow signs for the City Centre. Then as for North and West; From the South: Exit the M5 at Junction 19 and follow Taunton signs over the swing bridge (then as above).
Away Fans Car Parking: Bedminster Cricket Club, Clanidge Road, Bristol – SatNav: BS3 2JX (½ mile from Ashton Gate)
Bus Services: Services 27A and 28A from Bristol Temple Meads Station. A bus leaves Temple Meads 1 hour prior to kick-off.

BRISTOL ROVERS FC

Founded: 1883 **(Re-entered League**: 2015)
Former Names: Black Arabs FC (1883-84);
Eastville Rovers FC (1884-96);
Bristol Eastville Rovers FC (1896-97)
Nickname: 'Pirates' 'Rovers' 'Gas'
Ground: Memorial Stadium, Filton Avenue, Horfield,
Bristol   BS7 0BF
Pitch Size: 110 × 71 yards

Ground Capacity: 11,000
Seating Capacity: 3,307
Record Attendance: 12,011 (9th March 2008)
Colours: Blue & White quartered shirts, White shorts
Telephone Nº: (0117) 909-6648
Fax Number: (0117) 907-4312
Web Site: www.bristolrovers.co.uk

GENERAL INFORMATION

Car Parking: Very limited number of spaces at the ground
and street parking
Coach Parking: At the ground
Nearest Railway Station: Temple Meads (2 miles)
Nearest Bus Station: Bristol City Centre
Club Shop: At the ground
Opening Times: Monday to Friday, 9.00am to 5.00pm.
Open from 9.00am to 1.00pm on non-match Saturdays and
9.00am until kick-off then after the game on matchdays.
Telephone Nº: (0117) 909-6648 Option 1

GROUND INFORMATION

Away Supporters' Entrances & Sections:
Entrance to East Terrace & South Stand via Filton Avenue

ADMISSION INFO (2019/2020 PRICES)

Adult Standing: £19.00 – £21.00
Adult Seating: £23.00 – £25.00
Under-21s/ Concessionary Standing: £15.00 – £17.00
Under-21s/Concessionary Seating: £19.00 – £21.00
Under-16s Standing: £10.00
Under-16s Seating: £10.00 – £12.00
Under-11s Standing: £5.00
Under-11s Seating: £5.00 – £7.00
Programme Price: £3.00

FANS WITH DISABILITIES INFORMATION

Wheelchairs: 38 spaces in total including 10 spaces for
Away fans in front of the East Stand and West Stand
Helpers: One helper admitted per fan with disabilities
Prices: £7.00 to £12.00 (depending on age) for fans in
wheelchairs and the ambulant. Helpers are admitted free
Disabled Toilets: Available in the East Stand and West Stand
Contact: (0117) 909-6648 Option 1 (Bookings are necessary)
07557 443343 David Parker (Disability Liaison Officer) –
dave.parker@bristolrovers.co.uk

Travelling Supporters' Information: Routes: From All Parts: Exit the M32 at Junction 2 then take the exit at the roundabout
(signposted Horfield) into Muller Road. Continue for approximately 1½ miles passing straight across 3 sets of traffic lights. At the
6th set of traffic lights turn left into Filton Avenue and the ground is immediately on the left.

BURNLEY FC

Founded: 1882 (**Entered League**: 1888)
Former Name: Burnley Rovers FC
Nickname: 'Clarets'
Ground: Turf Moor, Harry Potts Way, Burnley, Lancashire BB10 4BX
Ground Capacity: 21,944 (All seats)
Record Attendance: 54,775 (23rd February 1924)

Pitch Size: 115 × 75 yards
Colours: Claret and Sky Blue shirts and shorts
Telephone Nº: (01282) 446800
Ticket Office: 0844 807-1882
Fax Number: (01282) 700014
Web Site: www.burnleyfootballclub.com
E-mail: info@burnleyfc.com

GENERAL INFORMATION

Car Parking: Matchday parking restrictions in surrounding streets so it is recommended that the various Town Centre car parks are used by visiting fans.
Coach Parking: By Police direction
Nearest Railway Station: Burnley Central (1½ miles)
Nearest Bus Station: Burnley (5 minutes walk)
Club Shop: At the ground and at Charter Walk Shopping Centre, 4 Fleet Walk, Burnley BB11 1QE
Opening Times: At Turf Moor: Monday to Friday and non-match Saturdays 10.00am – 4.00pm; Saturday matchdays open from 10.00am to kick-off then for 1 hour after the game. At Charter Walk: Monday to Saturday 9.00am to 5.30pm and Sunday 10.00am – 4.00pm.
Telephone Nº: (01282) 700016 or (01282) 453914

GROUND INFORMATION

Away Supporters' Entrances & Sections:
Ladbrokes Stand

ADMISSION INFO (2019/2020 PRICES)

Adult Seating: £30.00 – £40.00
Under-18s Seating: £15.00 – £20.00
Under-12s Seating: £10.00 (with a paying adult in the Family Stand only)
Under-22s/Senior Citizen Seating: £20.00 – £25.00
Programme Price: £3.00

FANS WITH DISABILITIES INFORMATION

Wheelchairs: 42 spaces available in the four designated wheelchair areas arounnd the ground.
Helpers: One helper admitted for each wheelchair user
Prices: Normal prices apply for fans with disabilities plus one helper admitted free of charge
Disabled Toilets: Available
Commentary radios are available to purchase for a nominal fee.
Contact: (01282) 446800 (Bookings are necessary) – Doug Metcalfe (DAO) – d.metcalfe@burnleyfc.com

Travelling Supporters' Information: Routes: From the North: Follow the A682 to the Town Centre and take first exit at roundabout (Gala Club) into Yorkshire Street. Follow through traffic signals into Harry Potts Way; From the East: Follow the A646 to the A671 then along Todmorden Road towards the Town Centre. At the traffic signals (crossroads) turn right into Harry Potts Way; From the West & South: Exit the M6 at Junction 29 onto the M65. Exit the M65 at Junction 10 and follow signs for Burnley Football Club. At the roundabout in the town centre take the third exit into Yorkshire Street. Then as from the North.

BURTON ALBION FC

Founded: 1950   (**Entered League**: 2009)
Former Names: None
Nickname: 'The Brewers'
Ground: The Pirelli Stadium, Princess Way, Burton-on-Trent   DE13 0AR
Record Attendance: 6,746 (vs Derby County, 2016)
Pitch Size: 110 × 72 yards

Colours: Yellow shirts with Black trim, Black shorts
Telephone Nº: (01283) 565938
Fax Number: (01283) 523199
Ground Capacity: 6,912   **Seating Capacity**: 2,034
Web site: www.burtonalbionfc.co.uk
E-mail: bafc@burtonalbionfc.co.uk

GENERAL INFORMATION

Car Parking: 400 spaces available at the ground (£5.00)
Coach Parking: Available at Claymills Pumping Station, Meadow Lane, Burton-on-Trent DE13 0DA (approximately 1 mile). Stewards will direct if necessary.
Nearest Railway Station: Burton-on-Trent (1½ miles)
Nearest Bus Station: Burton-on-Trent (1½ miles)
Club Shop: At the ground
Opening Times: Weekdays 8.30am to 5.30pm and Saturday Matchdays from 9.00am until 5.30pm (but only until noon on non-matchdays)
Telephone Nº: (01283) 565938

GROUND INFORMATION

Away Supporters' Entrances & Sections:
Main Stand and East Terrace

ADMISSION INFO (2019/2020 PRICES)

Adult Standing: £20.00   **Adult Seating**: £24.00
Under-17s Standing: £7.00 **Under-17s Seating**: £14.00
Ages 17 to 22 Standing: £15.00   **Seating**: £22.00
Senior Citizen Standing: £18.00   **Seating**: £22.00
Note: Cheaper 'Early bird' prices are available for tickets purchased before 5.00pm on the day before the game.
Programme Price: £3.00

FANS WITH DISABILITIES INFORMATION

Wheelchairs: Over 60 spaces available for home and away fans in designated areas (East Terrace for away fans).
Helpers: Admitted
Prices: Normal prices for fans with disabilities. Helpers free
Disabled Toilets: Available in all stands
Contact: (01283) 565938   (Bookings are necessary)

Travelling Supporters' Information:
Routes: From the M1, North and South: Exit at Junction 23A and join the A50 towards Derby (also signposted for Alton Towers). Join the A38 southbound at the Toyota factory (towards Burton & Lichfield) then exit for Burton North onto the A5121. Continue past the Pirelli factory on the right and the BP Garage and Cash & Carry on the left then turn into Princess Way at the roundabout; From the M5/6 South: Join the M42 northbound and exit onto the A446 signposted Lichfield. Follow signs for the A38 to Burton then exit onto A5121 as above; From the M6 North: Exit at Junction 15 and follow the A50 towards Stoke and Uttoxeter. Exit the A50 for the A38 southbound signposted Burton and Lichfield at the Toyota factory, then as above. SatNav users should enter the following post code: DE13 0BH

CAMBRIDGE UNITED FC

Founded: 1912 (**Re-entered League**: 2014)
Former Name: Abbey United FC (1912-1951)
Nickname: 'U's' 'United'
Ground: Abbey Stadium, Newmarket Road,
Cambridge CB5 8LN
Ground Capacity: 8,127
Seating Capacity: 4,376
Pitch Size: 110 × 74 yards

Record Attendance: 14,000 (1st May 1970)
Colours: Amber and Black striped shirts, Black shorts
Telephone Nº: (01223) 566500
Ticket Office: (01223) 566500 (Option 1)
Fax Number: (01223) 729220
Web Site: www.cambridge-united.co.uk
E-mail: info@cambridge-united.co.uk

GENERAL INFORMATION

Car Parking: Street parking or use Park and Ride
Coach Parking: Coldhams Road
Nearest Railway Station: Cambridge (2 miles)
Nearest Bus Station: Cambridge City Centre
Club Shop: At the ground
Opening Times: Monday to Friday 10.00am to 4.00pm
and Matchdays 10.00am to kick-off
Telephone Nº: (01223) 566500 Option 2

GROUND INFORMATION

Away Supporters' Entrances & Sections:
Coldham Common turnstiles 20-22 – Habbin Terrace (South)
and South Stand (Seating) turnstiles 23-26

ADMISSION INFO (2018/2019 PRICES)

Adult Standing: £18.00   **Seating**: £20.00 – £24.00
Junior Standing/Seating: £7.00
Under-18s Standing: £10.00   **Seating**: £10.00 – £20.00
Concessionary Standing: £14.00
Concessionary Seating: £15.00 – £20.00
Programme Price: £3.00
Note: Prices for the 2020/2021 season were not available at
the time of going to press. Please contact the club for details.

FANS WITH DISABILITIES INFORMATION

Wheelchairs: 35 spaces for Home fans in sections in front
of Main Stand and in the North Terrace. 10 spaces for Away
fans in the South Stand.
Helpers: One helper admitted per fan with disabilities
Prices: Normal prices apply for the disabled. Free for helpers
Disabled Toilets: Available
Contact: (01223) 566500 Option 8   (Early booking strongly
advised) – Andy Beattie (DLO) 07769 217870

Travelling Supporters' Information: From the North: Take the A14 from Huntingdon, then turn east along the A14 dual
carriageway. Exit the A14 at the 4th junction (to the east of Cambridge), up the slip road signposted Stow-cum-Quy then turn
right onto the A1303, returning westwards towards Cambridge. Go straight on at the first roundabout passing the Airport on
the left then straight on at two sets of traffic lights. Go straight on at the next roundabout and the ground is on the left after 700
yards; From the South: Exit the M11 at Junction 14 and turn east along the A14 dual carriageway. Then as from the North.
Bus Services: Services from the Railway Station to the City Centre and Nº 3 from the City Centre to the Ground.

CARDIFF CITY FC

Founded: 1899 (**Entered League**: 1920)
Former Names: Riverside FC (1899-1902) and Riverside Albion FC (1902-1908)
Nickname: 'Bluebirds'
Ground: Cardiff City Stadium, Leckwith Road, Cardiff CF11 8AZ
Record Attendance: 33,028 (22nd December 2018)
Ground Capacity: 33,316 (All seats)

Pitch Size: 110 × 75 yards
Colours: Blue shirts and shorts
Telephone Nº: 0333 311-1927
Ticket Office: 0333 311-1920
Fax Number: 0845 365-1116
Web Site: www.cardiffcityfc.co.uk
E-mail: club@cardiffcityfc.co.uk

GENERAL INFORMATION

Car Parking: Stadium car park and Street Parking
Coach Parking: Stadium car park (adjacent)
Nearest Railway Station: Cardiff Central (1 mile) and also Ninian Park Station (500 yards)
Nearest Bus Station: Cardiff Central
Club Shop: At the ground
Opening Times: Weekdays from 9.00am to 5.00pm and Saturdays 10.00am to 4.00pm
Telephone Nº: 0333 311-1922
Postal Sales: Yes (Internet Sales also accepted)

GROUND INFORMATION

Away Supporters' Entrances & Sections:
Grange End, Gate 07 – sections 119 to 122

ADMISSION INFO (2019/2020 PRICES)

Adult Seating: £17.00 – £34.00
Concessionary Seating: £13.00 – £29.00
Ages 16 to 21 Seating: £10.00 – £24.00
Under-16s Seating: £7.00 – £19.00
Note: Prices vary depending on the classification of the game and cheaper prices are available in the Family area.

FANS WITH DISABILITIES INFORMATION

Wheelchairs: Numerous spaces available for fans with disabilities in various areas around the ground
Helpers: One helper admitted per fan with disabilities
Prices: Normal prices for fans with disabilities. Helpers admitted free of charge
Disabled Toilets: Available – access via Radar Key system
Contact: 0333 311-1927 (Away fans tickets are normally sold in advance but may be available on the day) – Adam Gilliat (DAO) – adam.gilliat@cardiffcityfc.co.uk

Travelling Supporters' Information:
Routes: From All Parts: Exit M4 at Junction 33 and follow Penarth (A4232) signs. After 6 miles, take the B4267 to Cardiff City Stadium.

CARLISLE UNITED FC

Founded: 1903 (**Entered League**: 1928)
Former Names: Formed with the amalgamation of Shaddongate United FC and Carlisle Red Rose FC
Nickname: 'Cumbrians' 'Blues'
Ground: Brunton Park Stadium, Warwick Road, Carlisle   CA1 1LL
Ground Capacity: 17,300
Seating Capacity: 7,594

Record Attendance: 27,500 (5th January 1957)
Pitch Size: 112 × 74 yards
Colours: Royal Blue shirts and shorts
Telephone N°: 0330 094-5930
Ticket Office: 0330 094-5930 Option 1
Web Site: www.carlisleunited.co.uk
E-mail: enquiries@carlisleunited.co.uk

GENERAL INFORMATION

Car Parking: Rear of Ground via St. Aidans Road (£3.00)
Coach Parking: St. Aidans Road Car Park
Nearest Railway Station: Carlisle Citadel (1 mile)
Nearest Bus Station: Lowther Street, Carlisle
Club Shop: At the ground
Opening Times: Monday to Friday 10.00am – 5.00pm (and until 7.45pm for evening matches). Saturday Matchdays open 10.00am to 5.30pm (but closes at 3.00pm on other Saturdays).
Telephone N°: 0330 094-5930 Option 2

GROUND INFORMATION

Away Supporters' Entrances & Sections:
North End (Blocks 2 and 3) of the Pioneer Stand

ADMISSION INFO (2020/2021 PRICES)

Adult Standing: £19.00   **Seating**: £22.00
Senior Citizen Standing: £16.00   **Seating**: £19.00
Under-23s Standing: £13.00   **Seating**: £16.00
Under-18s Standing: £7.00   **Seating**: £10.00
Under-11s Standing: £4.00   **Under-11s Seating**: £7.00
Under-7s: Admitted free of charge
Note: Tickets are cheaper if purchased before the matchday
Programme Price: £3.00

FANS WITH DISABILITIES INFORMATION

Wheelchairs: 20 spaces for wheelchairs in a special section.
Helpers: One helper admitted per fan with disabilities
Prices: Fans in wheelchairs are admitted for £4.00. Helpers are admitted free of charge.
Disabled Toilets: Available throughout the ground
Contact: 0330 094-5930 Louise Banks (Bookings are recommended). E-mail: louise.banks@carlisleunited.co.uk

Travelling Supporters' Information:
Routes: From the North, South and East: Exit the M6 at Junction 43 and follow signs for Carlisle (A69) into Warwick Road for the ground; From the West: Take the A69 straight into Warwick Road.

CHARLTON ATHLETIC FC

Founded: 1905 (**Entered League**: 1921)
Nickname: 'Addicks'
Ground: The Valley, Floyd Road, Charlton, London, SE7 8BL
Ground Capacity: 27,111 (All seats)
Record Attendance: 75,031 (12th February 1938)
Pitch Size: 111 × 73 yards

Colours: Red shirts with White shorts
Telephone Nº: (020) 8333-4000
Ticket Office: 03330 144444
Fax Number: (020) 8333-4001
Web Site: www.cafc.co.uk
E-mail: info@cafc.co.uk

GENERAL INFORMATION

Car Parking: Street Parking
Coach Parking: By Police direction
Nearest Railway Station: Charlton (2 minutes walk)
Nearest Bus Station: At Charlton Railway Station as above
Club Shop: At the ground
Opening Times: Tuesday to Saturday 10.00am to 3.00pm
Telephone Nº: (020) 8333-4035

GROUND INFORMATION

Away Supporters' Entrances & Sections:
Valley Grove/Jimmy Seed Stand

ADMISSION INFO (2020/2021 PRICES)

Adult Seating: £20.00 – £37.00
Student Seating: £15.00 – £21.00
Senior Citizen/Under-21s Seating: £16.00 – £28.00
Under-18s Seating: £10.00 – £15.00
Under-11s Seating: £5.00
Programme Price: £3.00

FANS WITH DISABILITIES INFORMATION

Wheelchairs: 96 spaces available for Home fans around the ground. 7 spaces available for Away fans in the South (Jimmy Seed) Stand
Helpers: One helper admitted per fan with disabilities
Prices: Concessionary prices for disabled fans. Helpers free
Disabled Toilets: Available in West and East Stands
Commentaries are available – please ring for details
Contact: 03330 144444 (Ticket Office –Bookings are necessary) or contact Kishan Palmer (Disability Liaison Officer): (020) 8333-4000

Travelling Supporters' Information:
Routes: From All Parts: Exit the M25 at Junction 2 (A2 London-bound) and follow until the road becomes the A102(M). Take the exit marked Woolwich Ferry and turn right along the A206 Woolwich Road. After approximately 1 mile do a U-turn at the roundabout back along Woolwich Road. At the traffic lights turn left into Charlton Church Lane and Floyd Road is the 2nd left.

CHELSEA FC

Founded: 1905 (**Entered League**: 1905)
Nickname: 'Blues'
Ground: Stamford Bridge, Fulham Road, London, SW6 1HS
Ground Capacity: 41,631 (All seats)
Record Attendance: 82,905 (12th October 1935)
Pitch Size: 113 × 74 yards

Colours: Blue shirts and shorts
Telephone Nº: 0371 811-1955
+44 207 386-9373 (International callers)
Ticket Office: 0371 811-1905
+44 207 835-6000 (International callers)
Fax Number: (020) 7381-4831
Web Site: www.chelseafc.com
E-mail: enquiries@chelseafc.com

GENERAL INFORMATION

Car Parking: Pre-booked underground car park at ground
Coach Parking: By Police direction
Nearest Tube Station: Fulham Broadway (District)
Club Shop: Chelsea Megastore – at the ground
Opening Times: Monday to Saturday 10.00am – 5.00pm; Sundays 11.00am–5.00pm; Bank Holidays 11.00am – 5.00pm. Closed on home matchdays.
Megastore Telephone Nº: 0371 811 1955

GROUND INFORMATION

Away Supporters' Entrances & Sections:
Shed End

ADMISSION INFO (2020/2021 PRICES)

Adult Seating: £30.00 – £95.00
Child/Senior Citizen Seating: £18.00 – £27.50
Note: Concessionary tickets are available in the Family Stand, East Upper Stand, Shed Lower and Matthew Harding Lower stands.
Programme Price: £3.00

FANS WITH DISABILITIES INFORMATION

Seating: 258 spaces in total (including personal assistants) for Home and Away fans in the disabled area
Personal Assistants: One admitted per fan with disabilities
Prices: Free of charge for fans with disabilities
Disabled Toilets: Available around the ground
Free commentaries for blind supporters are available
Contact: 0371 811-2012 (Bookings are necessary) – Bob Flatau (DAO)

Travelling Supporters' Information:
Routes: From the North & East: Follow Central London signs from the A1/M1 to Hyde Park Corner, then signs for Guildford (A3) to Knightsbridge (A4). After 1 mile turn left into Fulham Road; From the South: Take the A13 or A24 then the A219 to cross Putney Bridge and follow signs for 'West End' (A304) to join the A308 into Fulham Road; From the West: Take the M4 then A4 to Central London, then follow signs to Westminster (A3220). After ¾ mile, turn right at crossroads into Fulham Road.

CHELTENHAM TOWN FC

Founded: 1887
Nickname: 'Robins'
Ground: Jonny-Rocks Stadium, Whaddon Road, Cheltenham, Gloucestershire   GL52 5NA
Ground Capacity: 7,200
Seating Capacity: 4,168
Record Attendance: 8,326 (1956)

Pitch Size: 110 × 72 yards
Colours: Red and White striped shirts, White shorts
Telephone Nº: (01242) 573558
Ticket Office: (01242) 573558 Option 1
Fax Number: (01242) 224675
Web Site: www.ctfc.com
E-mail: info@ctfc.com

GENERAL INFORMATION

Car Parking: Available at the ground for a £6.00 charge
Coach Parking: Please phone for details
Nearest Railway Station: Cheltenham Spa (2½ miles)
Nearest Bus Station: Cheltenham Royal Well
Club Shop: At the ground
Opening Times: Tuesday, Thursday and Friday 10.00am to 3.00pm. Also Saturday Matchdays from 12.00pm.
Telephone Nº: (01242) 573558 Option 2

GROUND INFORMATION

Away Supporters' Entrances & Sections:
Hazlewoods Stand (entrance from Whaddon Road)

ADMISSION INFO (2020/2021 PRICES)

Adult Standing: £17.00
Adult Seating: £21.00 – £22.00
Junior/Student Standing: £6.00
Junior/Student Seating: £8.00
Concessionary Standing: £13.00
Concessionary Seating: £15.00 or £16.00
Programme Price: £3.00

FANS WITH DISABILITIES INFORMATION

Wheelchairs: Accommodated in front of the Main Stand (use main entrance) and in the Colin Farmer Stand
Helpers: Admitted free of charge
Prices: Concessionary prices are charged
Disabled Toilets: Available in the Colin Farmer Stand, adjacent to the Main Stand and in the Social Club
Contact: (01242) 573558   (Bookings are necessary) – Tim Nichols (DLO) – tickets@ctfc.com

Travelling Supporters' Information:
Routes: The ground is situated to the North-East of Cheltenham, 1 mile from the Town Centre off the B4632 (Prestbury Road) – Whaddon Road is to the East of the B4632 just North of Pittville Circus. Road signs in the vicinity indicate 'Whaddon Road/ Cheltenham Town FC'.

COLCHESTER UNITED FC

Founded: 1937 (**Entered League**: 1950)
Former Names: The Eagles FC & Colchester Town FC
Nickname: 'U's'
Ground: Jobserve Community Stadium,
United Way, Colchester   CO4 5UP
Ground Capacity: 10,105 (All seats)
Record Attendance: 19,072 (27/11/48 – Layer Road)
Pitch Size: 112 × 72 yards

Colours: Royal blue and white striped shirts with
White shorts
Telephone Nº: (01206) 755100
Ticket Office: (01206) 755161
Fax Number: (01206) 715327
Web Site: www.cu-fc.com
E-mail: ticketing@colchesterunited.net

GENERAL INFORMATION

Car Parking: 700 spaces at the ground – pre-bookings only. The club recommends the use of the Park and Ride car park (access via Junction 28 of the A12 – Postcode CO4 5JA). The stadium is a 5-10 minute walk over Boxted Road bridge and the parking fee is £3.00.
Coach Parking: Drivers should liaise with with stewards upon arrival at the ground
Nearest Railway Station: Colchester North (1½ miles)
Nearest Bus Station: Colchester Town Centre (1½ miles)
Club Shop: At the ground
Opening Times: Weekdays 10.00am to 2.00pm, Saturday Matchdays 11.00am to 6.00pm and Midweek Matchdays 5.30pm to 10.00pm.
Telephone Nº: (01206) 755135

GROUND INFORMATION

Away Supporters' Entrances & Sections:
North Stand or East Stand (North End)

ADMISSION INFO (2019/2020 PRICES)

Adult Seating: £22.00 – £30.00
Concessionary Seating: £17.00 – £24.00
Ages 18 to 21 Seating: £18.00
Under-18s Seating: £13.50 – £16.50
Under-14s Seating: £5.50 – £8.50
Under-11s Seating: Free of charge
Note: A variety of discounted rates are available for tickets purchased a set number of weeks in advance of the game.
Programme Price: £3.00 (Free to ticket holders)

FANS WITH DISABILITIES INFORMATION

Wheelchairs: 40 spaces in total situated in all stands with lift access available where required.
Helpers: One helper admitted per wheelchair
Prices: Concessionary prices for fans with disabilities. Helpers are admitted free of charge.
Disabled Toilets: Available in each stand
Contact: (01206) 755161 or (01206) 755130 (Disability Liaison Officer: chris.saward@colchesterunited.net)

Travelling Supporters' Information:
Routes: The stadium is located just to the south of junction 28 of the A12 on the northern outskirts of Colchester. As parking near the stadium is limited, the club recommends the use of the Park and Ride car park which is situated just to the north of junction 28. The stadium is then a 5 to 10 minute walk. Alternatively, pre-book a space in the club car park.

COVENTRY CITY FC

Coventry City are playing at Birmingham City's St. Andrew's Stadium during the 2020/2021 season.

Founded: 1883 (**Entered League**: 1919)
Former Names: Singers FC (1883-1898)
Nickname: 'Sky Blues'
Ground: St. Andrew's Trillion Trophy Stadium, Birmingham B9 4RL
Ground Capacity: 29,409 (All seats)
Record Attendance: 51,455 (vs Wolverhampton Wanderers at Highfield Road on 29th April 1967)

Pitch Size: 109 × 74 yards
Colours: Sky Blue shirts and socks, White shorts
Telephone N°: (024) 7699-1987
Ticket Office: (024) 7699-2335
Postal Address: Sky Blue Lodge, Leamington Road, Ryton-on-Dunsmore, Coventry CV8 3FL
Web Site: www.ccfc.co.uk
E-mail: info@ccfc.co.uk

GENERAL INFORMATION
Car Parking: Street Parking + Birmingham Wheels (secure parking but not related to the club)
Coach Parking: Coventry Road
Nearest Railway Station: Birmingham New Street or Birmingham Moor Street (20 minutes walk)
Nearest Bus Station: Digbeth National Express Coach Station
Club Shops: At Arena Shopping Park, Classic Drive, Coventry CV6 6AS
Opening Times: Monday to Saturday 9.30am to 5.30pm (unntil 8.00pm on Thursdays) and Sunday 10.30am to 4.30pm
Telephone N°: (024) 7767-2021

GROUND INFORMATION
Away Supporters' Entrances & Sections:
Gil Merrick Stand, Coventry Road

ADMISSION INFO (2019/2020 PRICES)
Adult Seating: £20.00
Under-18s Seating: £10.00
Concessionary Seating: £15.00
Programme Price: £3.00

DISABLED INFORMATION
Wheelchairs: Spaces available in the Spion Kop Stand, Gil Merrick Lower Stand, Tilton Road Stand and West Paddocks
Helpers: One assistant admitted for each fan with disabilities
Prices: Normal prices apply for fans with disabilities. Helpers are admitted free of charge
Disabled Toilets: Available in the Spion Kop Stand, Family Stand, Gil Merrick Stand and Tilton Road Stand
Contact: (024) 7621-7673 or 07976 783251
Mark Hornby – mark.hornby@ccfc.co.uk

Travelling Supporters' Information: From All Parts: Exit M6 at Junction 6 and take the A38 (M) (Aston Expressway). Leave at 2nd exit then take first exit at roundabout along the Dartmouth Middleway. After 1¼ miles turn left on to Coventry Road.
Bus Services: Services 17, 58, 59 & 60 from Birmingham Centre stop at Cattell Road just to the south of the stadium and Services 97f stops at Garrison Lane just to the north of the stadium.

CRAWLEY TOWN FC

Founded: 1896 (**Entered League**: 2011)
Former Names: None
Nickname: 'Red Devils'
Ground: The People's Pension Stadium, Winfield Way, Crawley, West Sussex RH11 9RX
Record Attendance: 5,880 (2013)
Pitch Size: 113 × 72 yards

Colours: Red shirts and shorts
Telephone Nº: (01293) 410000 (Ground)
Ticket Office: (01293) 410000
Ground Capacity: 6,134
Seating Capacity: 3,295
Web site: www.crawleytownfc.com
E-mail: feedback@crawleytownfc.com

GENERAL INFORMATION

Car Parking: Free parking is available in William Reed car park at Broadfield Park (5 minutes walk).
Coach Parking: At the ground
Nearest Railway Station: Crawley (1 mile)
Nearest Bus Station: By the Railway Station
Club Shop: At the ground
Opening Times: Weekdays 10.00am to 4.30pm (closed on Wednesdays) and Saturday matchdays from 10.00am onwards. Mid-week matches also open from 6.00pm to kick-off then for 30 minutes after the game.
Telephone Nº: (01293) 410000

GROUND INFORMATION

Away Supporters' Entrances & Sections:
North Entrance for terrace and seating in the KR-L Stand

ADMISSION INFO (2020/2021 PRICES)

Adult Standing: £18.00
Adult Seating: £22.00 – £24.00
Under-21s Standing: £13.00
Under-21s Seating: £15.00 – £16.00
Under-18s Standing/Seating: £12.00
Under-16s Standing/Seating: £6.00
Under-11s Standing/Seating: Free of charge
Senior Citizen Standing: £14.00
Senior Citizen Seating: £17.00 – £20.00
Note: Tickets are cheaper when purchased in advance

FANS WITH DISABILITIES INFORMATION

Wheelchairs: Accommodated in the East or West Stands for home fans and the East Stand for away fans
Helpers: One helper admitted per fan with disabilities
Prices: Normal prices apply for fans with disabilities. Free of charge for helpers
Disabled Toilets: Available around the ground
Contact: (01293) 410000 (Bookings are necessary)

Travelling Supporters' Information:
Routes: Exit the M23 at Junction 11 and take the A23 towards Crawley. After ¼ mile, the Stadium is on the left. Take the first exit at the roundabout for the Stadium entrance.

CREWE ALEXANDRA FC

Founded: 1877 (**Entered League**: 1892)
Nickname: 'Railwaymen'
Ground: Alexandra Stadium, Gresty Road, Crewe, Cheshire CW2 6EB
Ground Capacity: 10,101 (All seats)
Record Attendance: 20,000 (30th January 1960)
Pitch Size: 100 × 73 yards

Colours: Red shirts with White shorts
Telephone Nº: (01270) 213014
Ticket Office: (01270) 252610
Web Site: www.crewealex.net
E-mail: info@crewealex.net

GENERAL INFORMATION

Car Parking: Car Park at the ground (spaces for 400 cars with a £3.50 fee)
Coach Parking: Car Park at the ground
Nearest Railway Station: Crewe (5 minutes walk)
Nearest Bus Station: Crewe Town
Club Shop: At the ground
Opening Times: Monday to Friday and Matchdays 9.00am – 5.00pm (until 7.45pm for Night matches)
Telephone Nº: (01270) 213014 Option 2

GROUND INFORMATION

Away Supporters' Entrances & Sections:
Whitby Morrison Ice Cream Van Stand

ADMISSION INFO (2020/2021 PRICES)

Adult Seating: £23.00 – £25.00
Senior Citizen Seating: £17.50 – £19.00
Under-17s Seating: £10.00 – £12.00
Under-11s Seating: £6.50 – £7.50
Note: Members qualify for cheaper prices. Family tickets are available in the Family Stand.
Programme Price: £3.00

FANS WITH DISABILITIES INFORMATION

Wheelchairs: Over 70 spaces are available for home fans and 14 spaces are available for away fans
Helpers: One helper admitted per fan with disabilities
Prices: £17.50 – £19.00 for each fan with disabilities and one helper
Disabled Toilets: Available in all Stands
Commentaries are available for the blind
Contact: (01270) 252610 or 07733 077611
Beverley Dyer – bdyer@crewealex.net (Bookings necessary)

Travelling Supporters' Information:
Routes: From the North: Exit the M6 at Junction 17 and take the Crewe (A534) road, and at Crewe roundabout follow signs for Chester into Nantwich Road. Then take a left turn into Gresty Road; From the South and East: Take the A52 to the A5020, then on to Crewe roundabout (then as from the North); From the West: Take the A534 into Crewe and turn right just before the railway station into Gresty Road. **SatNav users**: Please enter the following post code: CW2 6EB

CRYSTAL PALACE FC

Photo courtesy of Crystal Palace FC

Founded: 1905 (**Entered League**: 1920)
Nickname: 'Eagles'
Ground: Selhurst Park, Whitehorse Lane, London, SE25 6PU
Ground Capacity: 25,486 (All seats)
Record Attendance: 51,482 (11th May 1979)
Pitch Size: 110 × 74 yards

Colours: Red and Blue striped shirts with Blue shorts
Telephone Nº: (020) 8768-6000
Ticket Office: 0871 200-0071
Web Site: www.cpfc.co.uk
E-mail: info@cpfc.co.uk

GENERAL INFORMATION

Car Parking: Street Parking only
Coach Parking: Thornton Heath
Nearest Railway Station: Selhurst or Norwood Junction (both 5 minutes walk)
Nearest Bus Station: West Croydon
Club Shop: At the ground
Opening Times: Weekdays & Away Matchdays 9.00am to 5.30pm. Home Matchdays from 9.00am until 30 minutes after kick-off as well as 60 minutes after the final whistle.
Telephone Nº: (020) 8768-6100

GROUND INFORMATION

Away Supporters' Entrances & Sections:
Park Road for the Arthur Wait Stand

ADMISSION INFO (2019/2020 PRICES)

Adult Seating: £30.00 – £53.00
Concessionary Seating: £25.00 – £38.00
Junior Seating: £10.00 – £26.00
Note: Prices vary depending on the category of the game
Programme Price: £3.50

FANS WITH DISABILITIES INFORMATION

Wheelchairs: 128 spaces are available around the ground, most of which are on raised viewing platforms
Helpers: One helper admitted per wheelchair
Prices: Concessionary prices apply for fans with disabilities. Helpers are admitted free of charge
Disabled Toilets: Located in the Holmesdale Road Stand
Commentaries are available for 12 people
Contact: (020) 8768-6080 pam.groves@cpfc.co.uk
(Bookings are necessary)

Travelling Supporters' Information:
Routes: From the North: Take the M1/A1 to the North Circular (A406) for Chiswick. Take the South Circular (A205) to Wandsworth then the A3 to the A214 and follow signs for Streatham to the A23. Turn left onto the B273 after 1 mile, follow to the end, turn left into the High Street and then into Whitehorse Lane; From the East: Take the A232 (Croydon Road) to Shirley and join the A215 (Northwood Road). After 2¼ miles turn left into Whitehorse Lane; From the South: Take the A23 and follow signs for Crystal Palace (B266) through Thornton Heath into Whitehorse Lane; From the West: Take the M4 to Chiswick (then as North).

DERBY COUNTY FC

Founded: 1884 (**Entered League**: 1888)
Nickname: 'Rams'
Ground: Pride Park Stadium, Royal Way, Pride Park, Derby DE24 8XL
Ground Capacity: 33,597 (All seats)
Record Attendance: 33,475 (1st May 2006)
Pitch Size: 110 × 74 yards

Colours: White shirts with Black shorts
Telephone N°: 0871 472-1884
Ticket Office: 0871 472-1884   Option 1
Web Site: www.dcfc.co.uk
E-mail: derby.county@dcfc.co.uk

GENERAL INFORMATION

Car Parking: Spaces for 1,424 cars at the ground (available for permit holders only). A further 200 spaces are available at Derby Conference Centre on London Road (£5.00 charge)
Coach Parking: At the ground
Nearest Railway Station: Derby (1 mile)
Nearest Bus Station: Derby Central
Club Shop: DCFC Megastore at the ground
Opening Times: Monday to Saturday 9.00am – 5.00pm (from 10.00am on Tuesdays); Sundays 10.00am – 4.00pm
Telephone N°: 0871 472-1884 (Option 2)

GROUND INFORMATION

Away Supporters' Entrances & Sections:
South East Corner

ADMISSION INFO (2020/2021 PRICES)

Due to the introduction of a 'dynamic' pricing system, we suggest that fans contact the club for further details about admission prices for any particular game.
Programme Price: £3.00

FANS WITH DISABILITIES INFORMATION

Wheelchairs: 206 spaces available in total
Helpers: One helper admitted for each fan with disabilities
Prices: Normal prices for disabled fans. Helpers free of charge
Disabled Toilets: Yes
Contact: (01332) 667528 Emma Drury   (Bookings are necessary)

Travelling Supporters' Information:
Routes: From All Parts: Exit the M1 at Junction 25 and follow the A52 towards the City Centre until the ground is signposted on the left. Follow the signs for the ground.
From the Train Station: The Stadium is 10 minutes walk by way of a tunnel under the railway opposite Brunswick Inn, Station Approach. Then follow the footpath; Buses: A shuttle service runs from the bus station from 1.00pm until 2.45pm on Saturdays. A similar service runs from 6.00pm – 7.30pm for midweek games. Return shuttles are available post-match.

DONCASTER ROVERS FC

Founded: 1879
Former Names: None
Nickname: 'Rovers'
Ground: Keepmoat Stadium, Stadium Way, Doncaster   DN4 5JW
Record Attendance: 15,001   (1st April 2008)
Pitch Size: 110 × 72 yards

Colours: Red & White hooped shirts with White shorts
Telephone Nº: (01302) 764664
Ticket Office: (01302) 762576
Ground Capacity: 15,231   (All seats)
Web site: www.doncasterroversfc.co.uk
E-mail: info@clubdoncaster.co.uk

GENERAL INFORMATION

Car Parking: 1,000 spaces available at the ground   (£5.00)
Coach Parking: At the ground   (£20.00 fee)
Nearest Railway Station: Doncaster   (2 miles)
Nearest Bus Station: Doncaster   (2 miles)
Club Shop: At the ground
Opening Times: Monday to Saturday 10.00am to 4.00pm (until 8.00pm for midweek matches). Saturday Matchdays open 10.00am to kick-off then from full-time until 5.30pm.
Telephone Nº: (01302) 764667

GROUND INFORMATION

Away Supporters' Entrances & Sections:
Ellgia (North) Stand

ADMISSION INFO (2019/2020 PRICES)

Adult Seating: £21.00 – £22.00
Senior Citizen/Ages 22 to 24 Seating: £17.00 – £18.00
Ages 18 to 21 Seating: £13.00 – £14.00
Ages 12 to 17 Seating: £8.00
Under-12s Seating: £5.00
Note: Members prices are lower than those shown.
Programme Price: £3.00

FANS WITH DISABILITIES INFORMATION

Wheelchairs: 18 spaces available in total with Away fans accommodated in the North Stand
Helpers: Admitted
Prices: Normal prices for fans with disabilities. Helpers are admitted free of charge
Disabled Toilets: Available in all Stands   (Radar Key required)
Contact: (01302) 764668   (Bookings necessary)   Mark Hughesman (DLO) mark.hughesman@clubdoncaster.co.uk

Travelling Supporters' Information:
Routes: Exit the M18 at Junction 3 and follow the A6182 towards Doncaster. The stadium is approximately 1½ miles from the motorway and is well signposted so follow these signs. There are 1,000 car parking spaces available at the stadium and the cost is £5.00 per car. A number of businesses on the nearby business park also offer matchday parking for a similar charge. Bus services run from the town centre/interchange to the Stadium with a shuttle service back operating after the match.

EVERTON FC

Founded: 1878 (**Entered League**: 1888)
Former Names: St. Domingo's FC (1878-79)
Nickname: 'The Toffees'
Ground: Goodison Park, Goodison Road, Liverpool L4 4EL
Ground Capacity: 39,572 (All seats)
Record Attendance: 78,299 (18th September 1948)

Pitch Size: 110 × 74 yards
Colours: Blue shirts with White shorts
Telephone Nº: (0151) 556-1878
Ticket Office: (0151) 556-1878
Web Site: www.evertonfc.com
E-mail: everton@evertonfc.com

GENERAL INFORMATION
Car Parking: Corner of Priory Road and Utting Avenue
Coach Parking: Priory Road
Nearest Railway Station: Kirkdale
Nearest Mainline Railway Station: Liverpool Lime Street
Nearest Bus Station: Queen's Square, Liverpool
Club Shop: Evertonone Megastore in Walton Lane by the ground plus Evertontwo in Liverpool One Shopping Complex.
Opening Times: Evertonone: Monday to Sunday 10.00am to 4.00pm. Evertontwo: Monday to Saturday 10.00am to 5.00pm and Sundays 11.00am to 5.00pm.
Telephone Nº: (0151) 556-1878

GROUND INFORMATION
Away Supporters' Entrances & Sections:
Bullens Road entrances for Bullens Stand – Turnstiles 55-60

ADMISSION INFO (2019/2020 PRICES)
Adult Seating: £35.00 – £49.00
Junior Seating: £15.00 – £20.00
Senior Citizen Seating: £30.00

FANS WITH DISABILITIES INFORMATION
Wheelchairs: 153 spaces for home fans, 19 spaces for away fans in a special section.
Helpers: One helper admitted per wheelchair
Prices: Normal prices for fans with disabilities. Helpers free.
Disabled Toilets: Available in the section for disabled fans – Radar Key required (available from stewards if necessary). Commentaries are available for the blind
Contact: (0151) 530-5396 or (0151) 319-4033
Bendan Connolly (DAO) – brendan.connolly@evertonfc.com
(Bookings are necessary)

Travelling Supporters' Information:
Routes: From the North: Exit the M6 at Junction 26 onto the M58 and continue to it's end. Take the 2nd exit at the roundabout onto the A59 Ormskirk Road. Continue along into Rice Lane and go straight across at the next roundabout into County Road. After ½ mile, turn left into Everton Valley then bear left into Walton Lane for the ground; From the South & East: Exit the M6 at Junction 21A and take the M62 to it's end. Turn right at traffic lights onto A5088 Queen Drive and continue to the junction with Walton Hall Avenue then turn left into Walton Lane (A580) and the ground is on the right.
Bus Services: Services to the ground – 19, 20, F1, F2, 30

EXETER CITY FC

Founded: 1901   (**Re-Entered League**: 2008)
Former Names: Formed by the amalgamation of St. Sidwell United FC & Exeter United FC
Nickname: 'The Grecians'
Ground: St. James Park, Exeter, EX4 6PX
Ground Capacity: 8,696
Seating Capacity: 3,600
Record Attendance: 21,013 (4th March 1931)

Pitch Size: 114 × 73 yards
Colours: Red and White striped shirts, Black shorts
Telephone Nº: (01392) 411243
Ticket Office: (01392) 411243
Web Site: www.exetercityfc.co.uk
E-mail: reception@ecfc.co.uk

GENERAL INFORMATION

Car Parking: Parr Street, John Lewis and Bampfyled Street car parks
Coach Parking: Paris Street Bus Station (10 minute walk)
Nearest Railway Station: Exeter St. James Park (adjacent)
Nearest Bus Station: Paris Street Bus Station
Club Shop: At the ground
Opening Times: Monday to Friday 8.30am to 5.00pm and 11.00am to 5.30pm on matchdays.
Club Shop Telephone Nº: (01392) 411243 Option 3

GROUND INFORMATION

Away Supporters' Entrances & Sections:
St. James Road turnstiles for standing in the Marsh Kia St. James Road Stand or Blocks L and M of the IP Office Main Stand for seating.
Note: Cash is only taken on the Thatcher Gold Big Bank turnstiles. Away section tickets are sold at the booth adjacent to the St. James Road turnstiles.

ADMISSION INFO (2020/2021 PRICES)

Adult Standing: £17.00 – £18.00
Adult Seating: £23.00 – £24.00
Concessionary Standing: £14.00 – £15.00
Concessionary Seating: £20.00 – £21.00
Under-18s Standing: £6.00 – £7.00
Under-18s Seating: £11.00 – £12.00
Programme Price: £3.00

FANS WITH DISABILITIES INFORMATION

Wheelchairs: Accommodated in the IP Office Main Stand, Stagecoach Stand and the Big Bank.
Helpers: One assistant admitted per wheelchair
Prices: Free of charge for assistants. £14.00 – £20.00 for fans with disabilities in the wheelchair area.
Disabled Toilets: Available by the Big Bank Stand
Contact: (01392) 411243 (Bookings are necessary) – Nick Saunders (DLO) disability@exetercityfc.co.uk

Travelling Supporters' Information:
Routes: From the North: Exit the M5 at Junction 29 and follow signs to the City Centre along Heavitree Road. Take the 4th exit at the roundabout into Western Way and the 2nd exit into Tiverton Road then 2nd left into Stadium Way; From the East: Take the A30 into Heavitree Road (then as from the North); From the South & West: Take the A38 and follow City Centre signs into Western Way, then take the third exit at the roundabout into St. James Road.   (Follow the brown football signs from the M5)
Note: This ground is difficult to find being in a residential area on the side of a hill without prominent floodlights!

FLEETWOOD TOWN FC

Founded: 1997   (**Entered League**: 2012)
Former Names: Fleetwood FC (1908-1976), Fleetwood Town FC (1977-1996), Fleetwood Freeport FC (1997-2002)
Nickname: 'Cod Army'
Ground: Highbury Stadium, Park Avenue, Fleetwood   FY7 6TX
Record Attendance: 6,150 vs Rochdale (13/11/65)
Pitch Size: 110 × 71 yards

Colours: Red shirts with White Arms, White shorts
Telephone Nº: (01253) 775080
Ground Capacity: 5,137
Seating Capacity: 2,701
Web site: www.fleetwoodtownfc.com
E-mail: info@fleetwoodtownfc.com

GENERAL INFORMATION

Car Parking: Street parking only
Coach Parking: Drop off in Hatfield Road (FY7 7DT) then park opposite the Steamer Pub on Queen's Terrace (FY7 6BT)
Nearest Railway Station: Poulton-le-Fylde (7 miles)
Nearest Bus Station: No.1 and No.14 buses from Blackpool town centre (30 minute journey)
Nearest Tram Stop from Blackpool: Stanley Road
Club Shop: At the ground and Poolfoot Farm Sports Complex
Opening Times: Monday to Friday 9.00am to 5.00pm
Telephone Nº: (01253) 775080

GROUND INFORMATION

Away Supporters' Entrances & Sections:
Percy Ronson Terrace (turnstiles 1-3) for standing and Parkside Stand seating (turnstiles 1-2)

ADMISSION INFO (2019/2020 PRICES)

Adult Standing: £20.00 – £24.00
Adult Seating: £22.00 – £28.00
Senior Citizen/Under-25s Standing: £15.00 – £19.00
Senior Citizen/Under-25s Seating: £17.00 – £23.00
Under-16s Standing: £5.00 – £9.00
Under-16s Seating: £6.00 – £11.00
Note: Prices are cheaper for members
Programme Price: £1.00

FANS WITH DISABILITIES INFORMATION

Wheelchairs: Accommodated
Helpers: Admitted
Prices: Normal prices for the fans with disabilities. Free of charge for helpers
Disabled Toilets: Available
Contact: (01253) 775080   (Bookings are necessary)
Steve Beane (DLO)   steve.beane@fleetwoodtownfc.com – 07950 369687

Travelling Supporters' Information:
Routes: Exit the M6 at Junction 32 and take the M55 towards Blackpool. Exit the M55 at Junction 3 and follow the A585 towards Fleetwood for approximately 11½ miles. On the outskirts of town, you will reach a roundabout with Blackpool and Fylde college on your left. Continue straight on at this roundabout but then take the first turn on the left into Copse Road. After approximately 1 mile, branch left and turn left onto Radcliffe Road as you pass the Fire Station. Take the next right onto Stanley Road and the Stadium is at the bottom of the road on the left.

FOREST GREEN ROVERS FC

Founded: 1889   (**Entered League**: 2017)
Former Names: Stroud FC
Nickname: 'The Green Devils'
Ground: The New Lawn, Another Way,
Forest Green, Nailsworth, Gloucestershire, GL6 0FG
Record Attendance: 4,836 (3rd January 2009)
Pitch Size: 110 × 70 yards

Colours: Green and Black hooped shirts, Green shorts
Telephone N°: 0333 123-1889
Ticket Office: 0333 123-1889
Ground Capacity: 5,141
Seating Capacity: 2,000
Web site: www.fgr.co.uk
E-mail: reception@fgr.co.uk

GENERAL INFORMATION

Car Parking: At the ground plus Park and Ride from Stroud Road
Coach Parking: At the ground
Nearest Railway Station: Stroud (4 miles)
Nearest Bus Station: Nailsworth
Club Shop: At the ground
Opening Times: Matchdays 12.00pm until kick-off
Telephone N°: 0333 123-1889

GROUND INFORMATION

Away Supporters' Entrances & Sections:
EESI Stand (West Stand) – Turnstiles 9 and 10

ADMISSION INFO (2020/2021 PRICES)

Adult Standing: £18.00   **Adult Seating**: £23.00–£25.00
Senior Citizen Standing: £14.00
Senior Citizen Seating: £18.00 – £20.00
Under-16s Standing: £6.00
Under-16s Seating: £8.00 – £9.00
Under-11s Standing/Seating: Free of charge – £4.00
Under-21s Standing: £9.00
Under-21s Seating: £12.00 – £14.00
Note: Discounted prices are available for advance purchases

FANS WITH DISABILITIES INFORMATION

Wheelchairs: Accommodated in the Main Stand (East)
Helpers: Admitted
Prices: Normal prices for fans with disabilities. Helpers free
Disabled Toilets: Available
Contact: 0333 123-1889   (Enquiries required 72 hours in advance of the game) Dale Vince (DLO & Chairman)
(01453) 834860   dale.vince@fgrfc.com

Travelling Supporters' Information:
Routes: The ground is located 4 miles south of Stroud on the A46 to Bath. Upon entering Nailsworth, turn into Spring Hill at the mini-roundabout and the ground is approximately ½ mile up the hill on the left.

FULHAM FC

Founded: 1879 **(Entered League:** 1907)
Former Names: Fulham St. Andrew's FC (1879-1898)
Nickname: 'The Whites'
Ground: Craven Cottage, Stevenage Road, Fulham, London SW6 6HH
Ground Capacity: 19,000 (All seats – temporarily reduced due to redevelopment of the Riverside Stand)
Record Attendance: 49,335 (8th October 1938)

Pitch Size: 109 × 71 yards
Colours: White shirts with Black shorts
Telephone Nº: 0843 208-1222
Ticket Office: (020) 3871-0810
Web Site: www.fulhamfc.com
E-mail: enquiries@fulhamfc.com

GENERAL INFORMATION

Car Parking: Street Parking (Matchday restrictions apply)
Coach Parking: Stevenage Road/Fulham Palace Road
Nearest Railway Station: Putney (1 mile)
Nearest Tube Station: Putney Bridge (District) (1 mile)
Club Shop: At the ground and also 959-961 Fulham Road, SW6 5HY
Opening Times: At the ground: Monday to Saturday 9.00am to 5.00pm and Sundays 11.00am to 4.00pm
Telephone Nº: (0203) 871-0815

GROUND INFORMATION

Away Supporters' Entrances & Sections:
Putney End for the Putney Stand

ADMISSION INFO (2019/2020 PRICES)

Adult Seating: £30.00 – £45.00
Junior Seating: £15.00
Concessionary/Under-21s Seating: £25.00 – £40.00
Note: Prices vary depending on the category of the game and tickets may be cheaper if purchased in advance.
Programme Price: £3.50

FANS WITH DISABILITIES INFORMATION

Wheelchairs: 68 spaces in total with including 14 spaces for Away fans in the Putney End, Block 7, Gate 1
Helpers: One assistant admitted per fan with disabilities
Prices: Concessionary prices for fans with disabilities. One helper admitted free of charge for each fan in a wheelchair.
Disabled Toilets: Available – access via Radar Key system.
Contact: (020) 3871-0810 (Bookings necessary)
Disability Liaison Officer: Nicola Walworth contact on (020) 8336-7477 or via E-mail – nwalworth@fulhamfc.com

Travelling Supporters' Information:
Routes: From the North: Take the A1/M1 to the North Circular (A406), travel west to Neasden and follow signs for Harlesden A404, then Hammersmith A219. At Broadway, follow the Fulham sign and turn right after 1 mile into Harbord Street then left at the end for the ground; From the South & East: Take the South Circular (A205), follow the Putney Bridge sign (A219). Cross the bridge and follow Hammersmith signs for ½ mile, turn left into Bishops Park Road, then right at the end; From the West: Take the M4 to the A4. Branch left after 2 miles into Hammersmith Broadway (then as from the North).

GILLINGHAM FC

Founded: 1893 (**Entered League**: 1920)
Former Names: New Brompton FC (1893-1913)
Nickname: 'Gills'
Ground: MEMS Priestfield Stadium, Redfern Avenue,
Gillingham, Kent   ME7 2PE
Ground Capacity: 11,582 (All seats)
Record Attendance: 23,002 (10th January 1948)

Pitch Size: 114 × 75 yards
Telephone Nº: (01634) 300000
Ticket Office: (01634) 300000
Fax Number: (01634) 850986
Web Site: www.gillinghamfootballclub.com
E-mail: info@gillinghamfootballclub.com

GENERAL INFORMATION

Car Parking: Street parking
Coach Parking: Croneen's Yard Car Park in Railway Street
(5 minute walk)
Nearest Railway Station: Gillingham
Nearest Bus Station: Gillingham
Club Shop: Megastore in Redfern Avenue
Opening Times: Megastore is open Weekdays from 9.00am
to 5.00pm and Matchdays from 9.00am to 3.00pm
Telephone Nº: (01634) 300000

GROUND INFORMATION

Away Supporters' Entrances & Sections:
Priestfield Road End

ADMISSION INFO (2019/2020 PRICES)

Adult Seating: £24.00 – £27.00
Senior Citizen Seating: £21.00 – £27.00
Under-18s Seating: £8.00 – £9.00
Under-12s Seating: £8.00 – £9.00
Note: Tickets are £2.00 cheaper if purchased in advance
Programme Price: £3.00

FANS WITH DISABILITIES INFORMATION

Wheelchairs: 67 spaces in total for Home and Away fans
and helpers in special sections around the ground
Helpers: One helper admitted per fan with disabilities
Prices: Normal prices for fans with disabilities. Helpers free
Disabled Toilets: Available in all areas of the ground
Contact: (01634) 300000 (Bookings are necessary)
Disability Liaison Officer: Ben Reeves –
breeves@priestfield.com

Travelling Supporters' Information:
Routes: From All Parts: Exit the M2 at Junction 4 and follow the link road (dual carriageway) B278 to the 3rd roundabout. Turn
left onto the A2 (dual carriageway) and go across the roundabout to the traffic lights. Turn right into Woodlands Road after the
traffic lights. The ground is ¼ mile on the left.

GRIMSBY TOWN FC

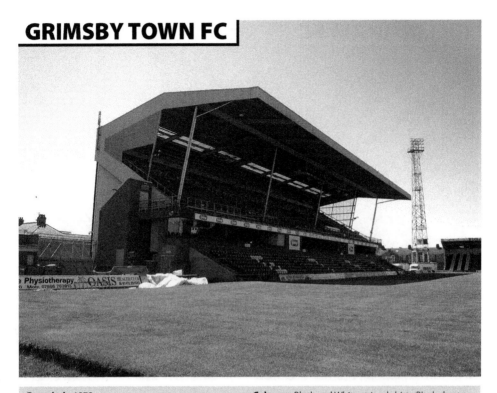

Founded: 1878
Former Names: Grimsby Pelham FC (1879)
Nickname: 'Mariners'
Ground: Blundell Park, Cleethorpes   DN35 7PY
Ground Capacity: 8,933 (All seats)
Record Attendance: 31,651 (20th February 1937)
Pitch Size: 111 × 74 yards

Colours: Black and White striped shirts, Black shorts
Telephone Nº: (01472) 605050
Ticket Office: (01472) 605050 (Option 4)
Web Site: www.grimsby-townfc.co.uk
E-mail: enquiries@gtfc.co.uk

GENERAL INFORMATION

Car Parking: Street parking
Coach Parking: Harrington Street – near the ground
Nearest Railway Station: Cleethorpes (1½ miles)
Nearest Bus Station: Brighowgate, Grimsby (4 miles)
Club Shop: At the ground
Opening Times: Monday – Saturday 10.00am to 2.00pm
but closed on Saturday Matchdays at present
Telephone Nº: (01472) 605050   Option 1

GROUND INFORMATION

Away Supporters' Entrances & Sections:
Harrington Street turnstiles 15-18 and Constitution Avenue turnstiles 5-14 for accommodation in the Osmond Stand

ADMISSION INFO (2020/2021 PRICES)

Adult Seating: £22.00
Senior Citizen/Student Seating: £15.00
Young Adults Seating (Ages 15–18): £15.00
Child Seating: £5.00 – £7.00 (Under-15s)
Note: Tickets are cheaper if purchased before the matchday

FANS WITH DISABILITIES INFORMATION

Wheelchairs: 20 spaces for home fans in the Main Stand and 20 spaces for away fans in the Osmond Stand
Helpers: Helpers are admitted
Prices: Normal prices for fans with disabilities. Helpers free
Disabled Toilets: Available
Commentaries are also available
Contact: (01472) 605050 (Bookings are necessary)
Amanda Jane Stephenson (SLO & DLO) – slo@gtfc.co.uk

Travelling Supporters' Information:
Routes: From All Parts except Lincolnshire and East Anglia: Take the M180 to the A180 and follow signs for Grimsby/Cleethorpes. The A180 ends at a roundabout (the 3rd in short distance after crossing docks), take the 2nd exit from the roundabout over the Railway flyover into Cleethorpes Road (A1098) and continue into Grimsby Road. After the second stretch of dual carriageway, the ground is ½ mile on the left; From Lincolnshire: Take the A46 or A16 and follow Cleethorpes signs along (A1098) Weelsby Road for 2 miles. Take the 1st exit at the roundabout at the end of Clee Road into Grimsby Road. The ground is 1¾ miles on the right.

HARROGATE TOWN AFC

Harrogate Town will be temporarily groundsharing with Doncaster Rovers at the Keepmoat Stadium (see page 35) during the early part of the season whilst a new grass pitch is laid. The club hope to be back playing home games at the Environment Stadium by November 2020.

Founded: 1919 (**Entered League**: 2020)
Former Names: Harrogate FC and Harrogate Hotspurs FC
Nickname: 'Town'
Ground: Environment Stadium, Wetherby Road, Harrogate HG2 7SA
Record Attendance: 15,000 (vs Sheffield Utd, 1920)
Pitch Size: 107 × 72 yards

Colours: Yellow and Black striped shirts, Black shorts
Telephone Nº: (01423) 210600
Ground Capacity: 5,000
Seating Capacity: 1,500
Web site: www.harrogatetownafc.com
E-mail: enquiries@harrogatetownafc.com

GENERAL INFORMATION

Car Parking: At the Kingsway Surgery on Wetherby Road or Cedar Court Hotel on Park Parade (£5.00 charge)
Coach Parking: At the ground
Nearest Railway Station: Harrogate (¾ mile)
Nearest Bus Station: Harrogate
Club Shop: At the ground
Opening Times: Monday to Friday 9.00am to 3.00pm and also on Matchdays
Telephone Nº: (01423) 210600

GROUND INFORMATION

Away Supporters' Entrances & Sections:
No usual segregation

ADMISSION INFO (2020/2021 PRICES)

Adult Standing: £18.00   **Adult Seating**: £19.00
Concessionary Standing: £14.00
Concessionary Seating: £15.00
Under-18s Standing: £8.00
Under-18s Seating: £9.00
Note: Under-5s are admitted free of charge and tickets are cheaper when purchased in advance.

DISABLED INFORMATION

Wheelchairs: Accommodated at the front of the Main Stand
Helpers: One helper admitted for each disabled fan
Prices: Free of charge for each disabled fan and helper
Disabled Toilets: Available
Contact: (01423) 210600 (Bookings are necessary)

Travelling Supporters' Information:
Routes: From the South: Take the A61 from Leeds and turn right at the roundabout onto the ring road (signposted York). After about 1¼ miles turn left at the next roundabout onto A661 Wetherby Road. The ground is situated ¾ mile on the right; From the West: Take the A59 straight into Wetherby Road from Empress Roundabout and the ground is on the left; From the East & North: Exit the A1(M) at Junction 47, take the A59 to Harrogate then follow the Southern bypass to Wetherby Road for the A661 Roundabout. Turn right towards Harrogate Town Centre and the ground is on the right after ¾ mile.

HUDDERSFIELD TOWN FC

Founded: 1908 **(Entered League**: 1910)
Nickname: 'Terriers'
Ground: The John Smith's Stadium, Huddersfield, HD1 6PX
Ground Capacity: 24,554 (All seats)
Record Attendance: 24,169 (30th September 2017)
Pitch Size: 115 × 76 yards

Colours: Blue and White striped shirts, White shorts and socks
Telephone Nº: (01484) 960600
Ticket Office: (01484) 960606
Web Site: www.htafc.com
E-mail: info@htafc.com

GENERAL INFORMATION

Car Parking: No spaces available at the ground but private car parks on Leeds Road and St. Andrew's Road (not associated with the club) charge around £6.00 to park.
Coach Parking: Adjacent car park
Nearest Railway Station: Huddersfield (1¼ miles)
Nearest Bus Station: Huddersfield
Club Shop: At the ground and in the Packhorse Shopping Centre in King Street, Huddersfield
Opening Times: At the ground: Monday to Saturday 9.00am to 5.00pm, Saturday Matchdays 9.00am to 3.00pm. Packhorse Centre: Monday to Saturday 9.00am to 5.00pm
Telephone Nº: (01484) 960636 or (01484) 430192

GROUND INFORMATION

Away Supporters' Entrances & Sections:
Adzorb South Stand

ADMISSION INFO (2019/2020 PRICES)

Adult Seating: £30.00
Under-18s Seating: £15.00
Under-8s Seating: £10.00
Concessionary Seating: £20.00
Note: Prices shown are for tickets purchased in advance.
Programme Price: £3.50

FANS WITH DISABILITIES INFORMATION

Wheelchairs: 177 spaces in total for home and away fans in the special sections in the Adzorb South Stand, Revell Ward Stand and Britannia Rescue Stand. Additional spaces are available for the ambulant and visually impaired.
Helpers: Admitted
Prices: £15.00 – £30.00 for fans with disabilities. Helpers free
Disabled Toilets: Available in the each of the sections
Commentaries are available for the blind.
Contact: (01484) 960606 Option 5 (Bookings necessary)
Disability Liaison Officer – sue.farrell@htafc.com

Travelling Supporters' Information:
Routes: From the North, East and West: Exit the M62 at Junction 25 and take the A644 and A62 following Huddersfield signs. Follow signs for the Galpharm Stadium; From the South: Leave the M1 at Junction 38 and follow the A637/A642 to Huddersfield. At the Ring Road, follow signs for the A62 to the Galpharm Stadium.

HULL CITY AFC

Founded: 1904 (**Entered League**: 1905)
Nickname: 'Tigers'
Ground: KCom Stadium, West Park, Hull   HU3 6HU
Ground Capacity: 25,586 (All seats)
Record Attendance: 25,030 (May 2010)
Pitch Size: 115 × 75 yards

Colours: Black and Amber shirts with Black shorts
Telephone Nº: (01482) 504600
Ticket Office: (01482) 505600 (Weekdays only)
Fax Number: (01482) 304882
Web Site: www.hullcitytigers.com
E-mail: info@hulltigers.com

GENERAL INFORMATION

Car Parking: Walton Street Car Park (£5.00), City Centre Car Parks and a Park & Ride scheme from Priory Park (£1.20)
Coach Parking: By Police direction
Nearest Railway Station: Hull Paragon Interchange
Nearest Bus Station: City Centre, Hull
Club Shop: Tiger Leisure Superstore at the Stadium and in the Prospect Centre, Prince's Quay.
Opening Times: Superstore: Monday to Saturday 9.00am to 5.00pm and until 5.30pm on Saturday matchdays.
Prospect Centre: Monday to Saturday 9.00am to 5.30pm and Sunday 10.30am to 4.30pm.
Telephone Nº: (01482) 504600 or (01482) 358362

GROUND INFORMATION

Away Supporters' Entrances & Sections:
North Stand

ADMISSION INFO (2019/2020 PRICES)

Adult Seating: £33.00
Senior Citizen Seating: £24.00
Under-23s Seating: £18.00
Under-16s Seating: £12.00
Under-11s Seating: £9.00

FANS WITH DISABILITIES INFORMATION

Wheelchairs: 131 spaces in total for Home and Away fans available around all the stands at both upper and lower level
Helpers: One helper admitted per fan with disabilities (subject to registration)
Prices: Normal prices for fans with disabilities. Helpers free.
Disabled Toilets: Available throughout the ground.
Lifts are available. Commentaries are available for the blind
Contact: (01482) 358303   (Bookings are not necessary)
Disability Liaison Officer – ann.holland@hulltigers.com

Travelling Supporters' Information:
Routes: From the West: Take the M62 then join the A63. Continue under the Humber Bridge as the road becomes the A63 Clive Sullivan Way and turn off at the slip road just before the flyover marked "Local Traffic/Infirmary". Take the 2nd exit at the roundabout into Rawling Way. Turn left at the next main set of traffic lights on A1105 Anlaby Road. Continue over the flyover then take a right turn into Walton Street. The car park is half way down this street after the Sports Arena; From the Humber Bridge: Follow signs for Hull City Centre – the road curves round to the left to join the A63 Clive Sullivan Way. Then as from the West; From the North: Take the A1079 towards Beverley then follow signs for the Humber Bridge and A164. Take the A63 sign-posted Hull City Centre and follow onto the A63 Clive Sullivan Way. Then as from the West.

IPSWICH TOWN FC

Founded: 1878 (**Entered League**: 1938)
Nickname: 'Town' 'Tractor Boys'
Ground: Portman Road, Ipswich IP1 2DA
Ground Capacity: 30,311 (All seats)
Record Attendance: 38,010 (8th March 1975)
Pitch Size: 110 × 72 yards

Colours: Blue shirts with White shorts
Telephone Nº: (01473) 400500
Ticket Office: 03330 05 05 03
Fax Number: (01473) 400040
Web Site: www.itfc.co.uk
E-mail: enquiries@itfc.co.uk

GENERAL INFORMATION
Car Parking: Portman Road and West End Road car parks
Coach Parking: West End Road car park
Nearest Railway Station: Ipswich (5 minutes walk)
Nearest Bus Station: Ipswich
Club Shop: Planet Blue Superstore at the ground
Opening Times: Weekdays 9.00am–5.00pm. Opening times on Matchdays vary. Please contact the club for details
Telephone Nº: (01473) 400501

GROUND INFORMATION
Away Supporters' Entrances & Sections:
Cobbold Stand

ADMISSION INFO (2019/2020 PRICES)
Adult Seating: £23.00 – £47.00
Child Seating: £3.00 – £34.00
Senior Citizen Seating: £17.00 – £41.00
Note: Prices may be subject to change.
Programme Price: £3.00

FANS WITH DISABILITIES INFORMATION
Wheelchairs: 103 spaces and 103 seats for home fans in the East of England Cooperative, South and North Stands upper and lower tiers. 10 spaces and 10 seats for away fans in the lower East of England Cooperative Stand only.
Helpers: One helper admitted per fan with disabilities
Prices: Concessionary prices charged for each fan with disabilities plus one helper.
Disabled Toilets: Available around the ground
Commentaries are available for the blind
Contact: (01473) 400556 – lee.smith@itfc.co.uk
(Bookings are necessary)

Travelling Supporters' Information:
Routes: From the North and West: Take the A1214 from the A14/A12 following signs for Ipswich West only. Proceed through Holiday Inn Hotel traffic lights and at the 3rd set of traffic lights turn right into West End Road. The ground is ¼ mile along on the left; From the South: Follow signs for Ipswich West, then as from the North and West above.

LEEDS UNITED FC

Founded: 1919 (**Entered League**: 1920)
Former Names: Formed after Leeds City FC were wound up for 'Irregular Practices'
Nickname: 'United'
Ground: Elland Road, Leeds LS11 0ES
Ground Capacity: 37,890 (All seats)
Record Attendance: 57,892 (15th March 1967)

Pitch Size: 115 × 74 yards
Colours: White shirts and shorts
Telephone N°: 0871 334-1919
Ticket Office: 0871 334-1992
Web Site: www.leedsunited.com
E-mail: reception@leedsunited.com or
Supporters' Liaison – questions@leedsunited.com

GENERAL INFORMATION

Car Parking: Large car parks adjacent to the Stadium plus Park and Ride from Temple Green
Coach Parking: Adjacent to the Stadium
Nearest Railway Station: Leeds City (1½ miles)
Nearest Bus Station: Leeds City Centre – specials from Swinegate, Sovereign Street and also Pudsey Bus Station
Club Shop: At the Stadium, in the White Rose Shopping Centre, at Leeds/Bradford Airport and in central Leeds at the Merrion Centre and Trinity Leeds.
Opening Times: At the ground: Monday to Saturday 9.00am to 5.30pm and Sunday 10.00am to 4.00pm. Similar times in the central Leeds stores but with some variations. Generally open a little later and stay open a little later.
Telephone N°: 0871 334-1919 (Option 5) at the Stadium or (0113) 242-5120 at the Merrion Centre

GROUND INFORMATION

Away Supporters' Entrances & Sections:
South East Corner or South Stand – Upper & Lower Tiers

ADMISSION INFO (2019/2020 PRICES)

Adult Seating: £31.00 – £44.00
Concessionary Seating: £26.00 – £31.00
Under-16s Seating: £10.00 – £18.00
Under-11s Seating: £5.00 – £9.00 (Family Stand only)
Note: Prices vary according to the category of game played and most tickets are cheaper if purchased in advance.

FANS WITH DISABILITIES INFORMATION

Wheelchairs: 131 spaces in total in special sections in the West, North, South and East Stands
Helpers: One helper admitted per fan with disabilities
Prices: Concessionary prices are charged
Disabled Toilets: Available around the ground
Commentaries via headphones in the West Stand
Contact: (0113) 367-6178 (Nicola Connelly – DLO) (Bookings are necessary)
E-mail: disabledinfo@leedsunited.com

Travelling Supporters' Information:
Routes: From the North: Take the A58 or A61 into the City Centre and follow signs to the M621. Leave the Motorway after 1½ miles and exit the roundabout onto the A643 into Elland Road; From the North-East: Take the A63 or A64 into the City Centre (then as from the North); From the South: Take the M1 to the M621 (then as from the North); From the West: Take the M62 to the M621 (then as from the North).

LEICESTER CITY FC

Founded: 1884 (**Entered League**: 1894)
Former Names: Leicester Fosse FC (1884-1919)
Nickname: 'Foxes'
Ground: King Power Stadium, Filbert Way, Leicester, LE2 7FL
Ground Capacity: 32,312 (All seats)
Record Attendance: 32,242 (August 2015)

Pitch Size: 110 × 72 yards
Colours: Blue shirts with White shorts
Telephone Nº: 0344 815-5000
Ticket Office: 0344 815-5000 (Option 1)
Web Site: www.lcfc.com
E-mail: lcfchelp@lcfc.co.uk

GENERAL INFORMATION

Car Parking: NCP Car Park (5 minutes walk). Some pre-booked spaces at the ground may be available (£17.00) and a Park and Ride service is available from Enderby
Coach Parking: Sawday Street
Nearest Railway Station: Leicester (1 mile)
Nearest Bus Station: St. Margaret's (1 mile)
Club Shop: At the ground
Opening Times: Monday to Saturday 9.00am to 6.00pm. Saturday Matchdays open 9.00am until kick-off then for 30 minutes after the game. Sundays open 10.00am – 4.00pm
Telephone Nº: 0344 815-5000 Option 7

GROUND INFORMATION

Away Supporters' Entrances & Sections:
At the corner of the North and East Stands – Turnstiles 40-49

ADMISSION INFO (2019/2020 PRICES)

Adult Seating: £26.00 – £50.00
Under-22s Seating: £24.00 – £44.00
Under-18s Seating: £20.00 – £34.00
Under-16s Seating: £14.00 – £25.00
Under-12s Seating: £7.00 – £15.00
Under-10s Seating: £5.00 – £12.00
Senior Citizen Seating: £24.00 – £44.00
Note: Prices vary depending on the category of the game.
Programme Price: £3.00

FANS WITH DISABILITIES INFORMATION

Wheelchairs: 186 spaces for wheelchairs plus 111 spaces for helpers accommodated at various levels in all stands
Helpers: One carer admitted per fan with disabilities
Prices: Reduced prices are available – Phone for details
Disabled Toilets: Available in all stands
Contact: 0344 815-5000 Option 4 – disability@lcfc.co.uk
Liaison Officer: 07162 294544 (Jim Donnelly)

Travelling Supporters' Information:
Routes: From the North: Take the A46/A607 into the City Centre or exit the M1 at Junction 21, take the A5460, turn right ¾ mile after the Railway Bridge into Upperton Road, then right into Filbert Way; From the East: Take the A47 into the City Centre (then as from the North); From the South: Exit the M1 at Junction 21 and take the A5460, turn right ¾ mile after Railway Bridge into Upperton Road, then right into Filbert Way; From the West: Take the M69 to the City Centre (then as from North).

LEYTON ORIENT FC

Founded: 1881　(**Re-entered League**: 2019)
Former Names: Glyn Cricket and Football Club (1881-86); Eagle FC (1886-88); Clapton Orient FC (1888-1946); Leyton Orient FC (1946-66); Orient FC (1966-87)
Nickname: 'O's'
Ground: The Breyer Group Stadium, Brisbane Road, Leyton, London　E10 5NF

Ground Capacity: 9,271 (all seats)
Record Attendance: 34,345 (21st January 1964)
Pitch Size: 110 × 76 yards
Telephone N°: (020) 8926-1111
Ticket Office: (020) 8926-1010
Web Site: www.leytonorient.com
E-mail: info@leytonorient.net

GENERAL INFORMATION
Car Parking: Street parking
Coach Parking: By Police direction
Nearest Railway Station: Leyton Midland Road (½ mile)
Nearest Tube Station: Leyton (Central)
Club Shop: At the ground
Opening Times: Weekdays and Home Matchdays 10.00am to 3.00pm
Telephone N°: (020) 8926-1009

GROUND INFORMATION
Away Supporters' Entrances & Sections:
East Stand

ADMISSION INFO　(2019/2020 PRICES)
Adult Seating: £20.00 – £32.00
Senior Citizen/Concessionary Seating: £18.00 – £29.00
Under-18s Seating: £7.00 – £29.00
Under-11s Seating: £3.00 – £29.00
Note: Tickets are cheaper when purchased in advance
Programme Price: £3.00

FANS WITH DISABILITIES INFORMATION
Wheelchairs: Spaces are available in the North, East and West Stands
Helpers: One helper admitted per fan with disabilities
Prices: Normal prices for fans with disabilities. Helpers free
Disabled Toilets: Available near the disabled sections
Contact: (020) 8926-1004 / 07944 436596　(Bookings are necessary) Lindsay Martin (DLO) l.martin@leytonorient.net

Travelling Supporters' Information:
Routes: From the North & West: Take A406 North Circular, follow signs for Chelmsford to Edmonton. After 2½ miles take the 3rd exit at the roundabout towards Leyton (A112). Pass the railway station, turn right after ½ mile into Windsor Road and left into Brisbane Road; From the East: Follow the A12 to London then the City for Leytonstone. Follow Hackney signs into Grove Road, cross Main Road into Ruckholt Road then turn right into Leyton High Road, turn left after ¼ mile into Buckingham Road and left into Brisbane Road; From the South: Take the A102M through the Blackwall Tunnel, follow signs for Newmarket (A102) to join the A11 to Stratford, then follow signs for Stratford Station into Leyton Road to the railway station (then as from North).

LINCOLN CITY FC

Founded: 1884 (**Re-entered League**: 2017)
Nickname: 'Red Imps'
Ground: LNER Stadium, Lincoln LN5 8LD
Ground Capacity: 10,120 (All seats)
Record Attendance: 23,196 (15th November 1967)
Pitch Size: 110 × 72 yards

Colours: Red and White striped shirts, Black shorts
Telephone Nº: (01522) 880011
Ticket Office: (01522) 880011
Fax Number: (01522) 880020
Web Site: www.weareimps.com
E-mail: admin@theredimps.com

GENERAL INFORMATION

Car Parking: No specific parking for visiting fans.
Street parking or the City Centre car parks are the only option.
Coach Parking: Please contact the club for details.
Nearest Railway Station: Lincoln Central
Club Shop: At the ground and at Waterside in Lincoln
Opening Times: Monday to Saturday 10.00am to 4.00pm
and Saturday Matchdays 10.00am until kick-off and then
after the final whistle until 5.30pm. Open from 10.00am until
kick-off on midweek matchdays.
Telephone Nº: (01522) 539399 or (01522) 690674

GROUND INFORMATION

Away Supporters' Entrances & Sections:
Stacey West Stand – Turnstiles 4 to 8

ADMISSION INFO (2019/2020 PRICES)

Adult Seating: £24.00 – £26.00
Junior/Junior Seating: £10.00 – £11.00
Concessionary Seating: £19.00 – £21.00
Note: Discounts are available for families and members.
Programme Price: £3.00

FANS WITH DISABILITIES INFORMATION

Wheelchairs: 37 spaces available for home fans and 6
spaces available for away fans in a special section
Helpers: One helper admitted per fan with disabilities
Prices: Helpers are admitted free of charge if the supporter
they are assisting is in receipt of the higher rate of disability
allowance or enhanced PIP.
Disabled Toilets: 5 available in total
Contact: (01522) 880011   (Bookings are necessary)
Heidi Langham (DLO) – dlo@theredimps.com

Travelling Supporters' Information:
Routes: From the East: Take the A46 or A158 into the City Centre following Newark (A46) signs into the High Street and take next left (Scorer Street and Cross Street) for the ground; From the North and West: Take the A15 or A57 into the City Centre, then as from the East; From the South: Take the A1 then A46 for the City Centre, then into the High Street, parking on the South Common or in the Stadium via South Park Avenue, turn down by the Fire Station.

LIVERPOOL FC

Founded: 1892 (**Entered League**: 1893)
Nickname: 'Reds'
Ground: Anfield Road, Liverpool L4 0TH
Ground Capacity: 54,000 (All seats)
Record Attendance: 61,905 (2nd February 1952)
Pitch Size: 110 × 75 yards

Colours: Red shirts, shorts and socks
Telephone N°: (0151) 264-2500
Ticket Office: 0843 170-5555
Fax Number: (0151) 261-8813
Web Site: www.liverpoolfc.com
E-mail: customerservices@liverpoolfc.com

GENERAL INFORMATION

Car Parking: None available in the immediate area
Coach Parking: Priory Road and Pinehurst Avenue
Nearest Railway Station: Kirkdale (¾ mile)
Nearest Bus Station: Paradise Street, Liverpool
Club Shop: At the ground, at Williamson Square and 'Liverpool One' in the City Centre, at 48 Eastgate Street, Chester CH1 1LE, at 9 Castle Lane, Belfast BT1 5DA
Opening Times: At Anfield: Monday to Saturday 9.00am to 5.30pm and Sunday 10.00am to 4.00pm; Chester: Monday to Saturday 9.00am to 5.00pm (until 6pm Thursday to Saturday) and Sunday 11.00am to 5.00pm; At Liverpool One: Monday to Saturday 9.30am to 7.00pm and Sunday 11.00am – 5.00pm; At Williamson Square: Monday to Saturday 9.00am to 6.30pm and Sunday 10.00am – 4.00pm; At Belfast: Monday to Saturday 9.30am to 5.30pm and Sunday 1.00pm to 5.00pm.
Telephone N°: (0151) 264-2368 (Anfield store)

GROUND INFORMATION

Away Supporters' Entrances & Sections:
Anfield Road

ADMISSION INFO (2020/2021 PRICES)

Adult Seating: £37.00 – £59.00
Senior Citizen Seating: £28.00 – £44.00
Young Adult Seating: £18.50 – £29.50
Junior Seating: £9.00
Programme Price: £3.00

FANS WITH DISABILITIES INFORMATION

Wheelchairs: 239 spaces in total around the ground including 24 spaces for away fans in the Anfield Road Stand.
Helpers: One helper is admitted per wheelchair but a second helper can sometimes be accommodated
Prices: £14.00 to £44.00 for fans with disabilities, dependent on age. One helper is admitted free of charge with each fan with disabilities.
Disabled Toilets: Two available in the Paddock, two in the Kop Stand and one in the Anfield Road Stand
Commentaries are available for the visually impaired on request
Contact: (0151) 264-2500 Option 2 (Bookings are necessary)
Simon Thornton (DAO) – simon.thornton@liverpoolfc.com
(0151) 432-5678

Travelling Supporters' Information:
Routes: From the North: Exit the M6 at Junction 28 and follow Liverpool A580 signs into Walton Hall Avenue, pass Stanley Park and turn left into Anfield Road; From the South and East: Take the M62 to the end of the motorway, then turn right into Queen's Drive (A5058) and turn left after 3 miles into Utting Avenue. After 1 mile, turn right into Anfield Road; From North Wales: Take the Mersey Tunnel into the City Centre and follow signs for Preston (A580) into Walton Hall Avenue. Turn right into Anfield Road before Stanley Park.

LUTON TOWN FC

Founded: 1885 (**Re-entered League**: 2014)
Former Names: The club was formed by the amalgamation of Wanderers FC and Excelsior FC
Nickname: 'Hatters'
Ground: Kenilworth Road Stadium, 1 Maple Road, Luton LU4 8AW
Ground Capacity: 10,413 (All seats)
Record Attendance: 30,069 (4th March 1959)

Pitch Size: 110 × 72 yards
Colours: Orange shirts with Blue shorts
Telephone Nº: (01582) 411622
Ticket Office: (01582) 416976
Fax Number: (01582) 405070
Web Site: www.lutontown.co.uk
E-mail: info@lutontown.co.uk

GENERAL INFORMATION

Car Parking: Street parking is limited so the club recommends using Luton train station car park
Coach Parking: Luton Bus Station
Nearest Railway Station: Luton (1 mile)
Nearest Bus Station: Bute Street, Luton
Club Shop: Kenilworth Road Forecourt and also at Park Street in Luton town centre
Opening Times: 10.00am to 5.00pm
Telephone Nº: (01582) 411622 Option 4 (Park Street)

GROUND INFORMATION

Away Supporters' Entrances & Sections:
Oak Road for the Oak Stand

ADMISSION INFO (2020/2021 PRICES)

Adult Seating: £20.00 – £30.00
Under-10s Seating: £3.00 – £9.00
Under-17s Seating: £6.00 – £12.00
Under-19s Seating: £12.00 – £20.00
Under-22s Seating: £15.00 – £23.00
Senior Citizen Seating: £15.00 – £23.00
Over-75s Seating: £12.00 – £20.00
Note: Prices vary depending on the category of the game

FANS WITH DISABILITIES INFORMATION

Wheelchairs: 18 spaces for Home fans and 10 spaces for Away fans in the disabled section, Kenilworth Road End and Main Stand
Helpers: One helper admitted per disabled person
Prices: Concessionary prices for the disabled. Helpers free
Disabled Toilets: Available adjacent to the disabled area
Contact: (01582) 411622 (Bookings are necessary)
Stephen Copp (DAO) – stephen.copp@lutontown.co.uk
(07754 005567)

Travelling Supporters' Information:
Routes: From the North and West: Exit the M1 at Junction 11 and follow signs for Luton (A505) into Dunstable Road. Follow the one-way system and turn right back towards Dunstable, take the second left into Ash Road for the ground; From the South and East: Exit the M1 at Junction 10 (or A6/A612) into Luton Town Centre and follow signs into Dunstable Road. After the railway bridge, take the sixth turning on the left into Ash Road for the ground.

MANCHESTER CITY FC

Founded: 1887 (**Entered League**: 1892)
Former Name: St.Mark's FC, Ardwick FC (1887-1894)
Nickname: 'Cityzens' 'City' 'Blues'
Ground: Etihad Stadium, Etihad Campus, Manchester M11 3FF
Ground Capacity: 55,097 (All seats)
Record Attendance: 54,693 (February 2016)

Pitch Size: 115 × 75 yards
Colours: Sky Blue shirtswith White shorts
Telephone Nº: (0161) 444-1894 Option 5
Ticket Office: (0161) 444-1894 Options 2 then 1
Fax Number: (0161) 438-7999
Web Site: www.mancity.com
E-mail: mancity@mancity.com

GENERAL INFORMATION

Car Parking: 1,000 spaces available at the stadium. Another 7,000 spaces are available off site in the vicinity.
Coach Parking: Around 40 spaces available at the stadium
Nearest Railway Station: Ashburys (15 minutes walk) or Manchester Piccadilly (20 minutes walk)
Nearest Bus Station: 53,54,185,186,216,217,230,231,232, 233,234,235,236,237,X36 & X37 services stop at the stadium
Club Shop: At the stadium
Opening Times: Monday to Saturday 9.00am to 5.30pm, Sundays 11.00am to 5.00pm and before and after matches.
Telephone Nº: (0161) 444-1894 Option 3

GROUND INFORMATION

Away Supporters' Entrances & Sections: South Stand

ADMISSION INFO (2019/2020 PRICES)

Adult Seating: £31.50 – £76.50
Concessionary Seating: £24.50 – £60.50
Ages 18 to 21 Seating: £24.50 – £60.50
Junior Seating: £17.50 – £50.50
Programme Price: £3.00

FANS WITH DISABILITIES INFORMATION

Wheelchairs: 255 spaces available in total including 21 for away fans
Helpers: One helper admitted per disabled fan
Prices: Concessionary prices for the disabled. Helpers free
Disabled Toilets: 42 wheelchair accessible toilets are available around the stadium
Commentaries for the blind and lifts are also available
Contact: (0161) 438-7834 (Bookings are recommended)
Jon Dyster (Access Manager) – jon.dyster@mancity.com

Travelling Supporters' Information:
Routes: From the North: Exit the M60 at Junction 23 onto the A635 then turn right onto the A662 Ashton New Road. The stadium is approximately 1½ miles on the right hand side; From the East: Exit the M60 at Junction 24 and follow the A57 into Manchester before turning right onto the A6010 for the stadium; From the South: Follow the A6 into Manchester and then turn right onto the A6010 for the stadium. Alternatively, exit the M60 at Junction 1 and follow the A34 Kingsway into Manchester before turning right onto the A6010 for the stadium; From the West: Take the M602 into Manchester and continue onto the A57 then the A57(M) Mancunian Way onto the A635. Follow the road right before turning left onto the A6010 for the stadium.

MANCHESTER UNITED FC

Founded: 1878 (**Entered League**: 1892)
Former Names: Newton Heath LYR FC (1878-1892), Newton Heath FC (1892-1902)
Nickname: 'Red Devils'
Ground: Sir Matt Busby Way, Old Trafford, Manchester M16 0RA
Ground Capacity: 74,994 (All seats)
Record Attendance: 76,962 (25th March 1939)

Pitch Size: 115 × 76 yards
Colours: Red shirts with White shorts
Telephone Nº: (0161) 868-8000 Option 4
Ticket Information: (0161) 868-8000 Option 1
Fax Number: (0161) 868-8804
Web Site: www.manutd.com
E-mail: enquiries@manutd.co.uk

GENERAL INFORMATION

Car Parking: Lancashire Cricket Ground and Car Park E3 on John Gilbert Way. Other approved car parks are signposted
Coach Parking: By Police direction
Nearest Railway Station: At the ground
Nearest Bus Station: Chorlton Street
Nearest Metro Station: Old Trafford (located at L.C.C.C.) and also Salford Quays
Club Shop: At the ground
Opening Times: Non-matchdays: Monday to Saturday 10.00am – 5.00pm and Sundays 11.00am to 5.00pm. Saturday Matchdays 9.00am to 5.30pm for early kick-offs, 9.30am to 6.00pm (3pm kick-off), 9.30am to 8.30pm (5.30pm kick-off) and 9.30am to 10.45pm (8.00pm kick-off). Sundays 10.30am – 4.30pm (1.30pm kick-off) and 10.00am to 4.00pm (4.00pm kick-off).
Magastore Telephone Nº: (0161) 868-8567
Museum & Tour Centre: (0161) 868-8000 (Option 3)

GROUND INFORMATION

Away Supporters' Entrances & Sections: Bobby Charlton (South) Stand (turnstile 22) & East Stand (turnstile 30)

ADMISSION INFO (2020/2021 PRICES)

Adult Seating: £36.00 – £58.00
Concessionary/Under-18s Seating: £22.00 – £28.00
Ages 18 to 20 Seating: £29.00 – £45.50
Under-16s Seating: £13.00
Programme Price: £3.50

FANS WITH DISABILITIES INFORMATION

Wheelchairs: 160 spaces in total for Home and Away fans in sections in the North East & North West quadrants
Helpers: One helper admitted per fan with disabilities
Prices: Concessionary prices charge for fans with disabilities. Helpers are admitted free of charge
Disabled Toilets: Available
Commentaries are available for the visually impaired
Contact: (0161) 868-8009 (Bookings are necessary)
E-mail: accessibility@manutd.co.uk

Travelling Supporters' Information:
Routes: From the North and West: Take the M61 to the M60 and exit at Junction 4 following Manchester (A5081) signs. Turn right after 2½ miles into Sir Matt Busby Way for the ground; From the South: Exit the M6 at Junction 19 and take Stockport (A556) road then Altrincham (A56). From Altrincham follow Manchester signs and turn left into Sir Matt Busby Way after 6 miles; From the East: Exit the M62 at Junction 17 and take the A56 to Manchester. Follow signs for the South then signs for Chester (Chester Road). Turn right into Sir Matt Busby Way after 2 miles.

MANSFIELD TOWN FC

Founded: 1897 **(Re-entered League**: 1892)
Former Name: Mansfield Wesleyans FC (1897-1905)
Nickname: 'Stags'
Ground: One Call Stadium, Quarry Lane, Mansfield, Nottinghamshire NG18 5DA
Ground Capacity: 9,376 (All seats)
Record Attendance: 24,467 (10th January 1953)
Pitch Size: 110 × 70 yards

Colours: Amber shirts with Royal Blue piping, Royal Blue shorts with Amber flash
Telephone Nº: (01623) 482482
Ticket Office: (01623) 482482
Fax Number: (01623) 482495
Web Site: www.mansfieldtown.net
E-mail: info@mansfieldtown.net

GENERAL INFORMATION

Car Parking: Small car park at the ground (£5.00)
Coach Parking: Adjacent to the ground
Nearest Railway Station: Mansfield (5 minutes walk)
Nearest Bus Station: Mansfield
Club Shop: In the South Stand of the Stadium
Opening Times: Weekdays 10.00am – 5.00pm and Matchdays 10.00am – 3.00pm
Telephone Nº: (01623) 482482

GROUND INFORMATION

Away Supporters' Entrances & Sections:
North Stand turnstiles for North Stand seating

ADMISSION INFO (2020/2021 PRICES)

Adult Seating: £24.50 – £25.50
Senior Citizen Seating: £20.50 – £21.50
Young Adult Seating: £18.50
Junior Seating: £14.50 – £16.50
Under-7s Seating: Free of charge
Note: There is a £2.00 discount for tickets bought in advance.

FANS WITH DISABILITIES INFORMATION

Wheelchairs: 90 spaces available in total in special sections in the North Stand, Quarry Street Stand and West Stand
Helpers: Admitted
Prices: Normal prices apply for the disabled. Free for helpers
Disabled Toilets: Available in the North Stand, West Stand and Quarry Lane Stand
Contact: (01623) 482482   (Please buy tickets in advance)
Alan Lakin (DLO) – safetyofficer@mansfieldtown.net

Travelling Supporters' Information:
Routes: From the North: Exit the M1 at Junction 29 and take the A617 to Mansfield. After 6¼ miles turn right at the Leisure Centre into Rosemary Street. Carry on to Quarry Lane and turn right; From the South and West: Exit the M1 at Junction 28 and take the A38 to Mansfield. After 6½ miles turn right at the crossroads into Belvedere Street then turn right after ¼ mile into Quarry Lane; From the East: Take the A617 to Rainworth, turn left at the crossroads after 3 miles into Windsor Road and turn right at the end into Nottingham Road, then left into Quarry Lane.

MIDDLESBROUGH FC

Founded: 1876 (**Entered League**: 1899)
Nickname: 'Boro'
Ground: Riverside Stadium, Middlesbrough, TS3 6RS
Ground Capacity: 33,742 (All seats)
Record Attendance: 34,836 (28th December 2004)
Pitch Size: 115 × 75 yards

Colours: Shirts are Red with White detailing, shorts are White
Telephone Nº: (01642) 929420
Ticket Office: (01642) 929421
Web Site: www.mfc.co.uk
E-mail: ticket@mfc.co.uk

GENERAL INFORMATION

Car Parking: 1,250 spaces available at the stadium – permit holders only. Otherwise use town centre parking.
Coach Parking: At the ground – Car Park D
Nearest Railway Station: Middlesbrough (½ mile)
Nearest Bus Station: Middlesbrough
Club Shops: At ground
Opening Times: Weekdays 9.00am to 5.00pm, Saturday Matchdays 9.00am to 3.00pm then 5.00pm to 6.00pm.
Telephone Nº: (01642) 929422

GROUND INFORMATION

Away Supporters' Entrances & Sections:
East Stand

ADMISSION INFO (2019/2020 PRICES)

Adult Seating: £30.00 – £34.00
Senior Citizen Seating: £20.00 – £26.00
Under-18s Seating: £17.00
Note: Lower prices are available in the Family Zone and discounted prices are available for members.
Programme Price: £2.00

FANS WITH DISABILITIES INFORMATION

Wheelchairs: 81 spaces for home fans with 10 spaces for away fans in the East Stand
Helpers: One helper admitted per fan with disabilities
Prices: Normal prices for fans with disabilities. Helpers are admitted free of charge.
Disabled Toilets: Available in every stand with access via the Radar Key system
Contact: (01642) 929421   (Bookings are necessary)
Jade Johnson (DLO) – jade.johnson@mfc.co.uk

Travelling Supporters' Information:
Routes: From the North: Take the A19 across the flyover and join the A66 (Eastbound). At the end of the flyover, turn left at North Ormesby where the ground is well-signposted. The ground is 200 metres down the road; From the South: Take the A1 and A19 to the junction with the A66 (Eastbound). After the flyover, turn left at North Ormesby following signs for the ground.

MILLWALL FC

Founded: 1885 (**Entered League:** 1920)
Former Names: Millwall Rovers FC (1885-1893); Millwall Athletic FC (1893-1925)
Nickname: 'The Lions'
Ground: The Den, Zampa Road, London SE16 3LN
Ground Capacity: 20,146 (All seats)
Record Attendance: 20,093 (10th January 1994)

Pitch Size: 116 × 74 yards
Colours: Dark Blue shirts with White shorts
Telephone N°: (020) 7232-1222
Ticket Office: (020) 7740-3470
Web Site: www.millwallfc.co.uk
E-mail: slo@millwallplc.com

GENERAL INFORMATION

Car Parking: Street parking
Coach Parking: Adjacent to the ground
Nearest Railway Station: New Cross Gate (1 mile), Surrey Quays (1 mile) or South Bermondsey (½ mile)
Nearest Tube: New Cross Gate (1 mile)/Canada Water (1 mile)
Club Shop: Next to the Stadium
Opening Times: Daily from 9.30am to 5.00pm
Telephone N°: (020) 7231-9845

GROUND INFORMATION

Away Supporters' Entrances & Sections:
North Stand turnstiles 31-36. A walkway from South Bermondsey Station to the ground is open on matchdays

ADMISSION INFO (2020/2021 PRICES)

Adult Seating: £20.00 – £32.00
Under-18s Seating: £11.00 – £18.00
Under-16s: £10.00 – £14.00   **Under-12s:** £5.00 – £9.00
Concessionary Seating: £14.00 – £22.00
Note: Prices vary depending on the category of the game
Programme Price: £3.00

FANS WITH DISABILITIES INFORMATION

Wheelchairs: 36 spaces for home fans in the Barry Kitchener Stand plus 10 spaces for away fans in front of the North Stand
Helpers: One helper admitted per wheelchair
Prices: Standard prices for fans with disabilities. Helpers free
Disabled Toilets: 17 toilets available around the Stadium
Commentaries are available for the blind
Contact: (020) 7232-1222 (Bookings are necessary)
Shona Greaves (DLO) – slo@millwallplc.com

Travelling Supporters' Information:
Routes: From the North: Follow City signs from the M1/A1 then signs for Shoreditch & Whitechapel. Follow Ring Road signs for Dover, cross over Tower Bridge and after 1 mile take 1st exit at the roundabout onto the A2. From Elephant and Castle take the A2 (New Kent Road) into Old Kent Road and turn left after 4 miles into Ilderton Road to Zampa Road; From the South: Take the A20 & A21 following signs to London. At New Cross follow signs for Surrey Quays into Kender Street, turn left into Old Kent Road then right into Ilderton Road. Zampa Road is the 7th turning on the right; From the East: Take the A2 to New Cross (then as from the South); From the West: From M4 & M3 follow the South Circular (A205) then follow signs for Clapham, the City (A3) then Camberwell to New Cross and then as from South.

MILTON KEYNES DONS FC

Founded: 2004
Former Names: None
Nickname: 'Dons'
Ground: Stadium MK, Stadium Way West, Milton Keynes   MK1 1ST
Ground Capacity: 30,500 (All seats)
Record Attendance: 28,521
           (vs Liverpool, 25th September 2019)

Pitch Size: 115 × 74 yards
Colours: White shirts and shorts
Telephone N°: (01908) 622922
Ticket Office: (01908) 622933
Web Site: www.mkdons.com
E-mail: info@mkdons.com

GENERAL INFORMATION

Car Parking: 1,600 Pay and Display spaces at Stadium MK (£7.00 charge). Disabled drivers can park free of charge on production of a valid blue badge (entry via Saxon Street).
Coach Parking: By Police direction
Nearest Railway Station: Bletchley (1 mile)
Nearest Bus Station: Bletchley
Club Shop: At the Stadium
Opening Times: Weekdays 10.00am to 4.00pm
Telephone N°: (01908) 622973

GROUND INFORMATION

Away Supporters' Entrances & Sections:
North Stand corner, Gate 3

ADMISSION INFO (2020/2021 PRICES)

Adult Seating: £22.00 – £32.00
Concessionary Seating: £17.00 – £27.00
Under-18s Seating: £7.00 – £17.00
Programme Price: £3.00
Note: Under-12s are admitted free with a paying adult

FANS WITH DISABILITIES INFORMATION

Wheelchairs: A total of 123 spaces are available around the ground at concourse level, 93 for home fans, 20 for away fans
Helpers: One helper admitted per fan with disabilities
Prices: Normal prices for fans with disabilities. Helpers are admitted free of charge
Disabled Toilets: Available throughout the stadium
Contact: (01908) 622999   (Bookings are necessary) –
E-mail: disability@mkdons.com or contact Andy Standen andy.standen@stadiummk.com

Travelling Supporters' Information:
Routes: From all parts: Exit the M1 at Junction 14, following signs for Milton Keynes and cross the first roundabout onto H6 Childs Way. Turn left at the next roundabout onto V11 Tongwell Street. Continue along this road then turn right at the third roundabout onto H9 Groveway. Continue along Groveway then take the first exit at the fourth roundabout towards Central Bletchley. Stadium:MK is the first turning on the left.

MORECAMBE FC

Founded: 1920   (**Entered League**: 2007)
Former Names: None
Nickname: 'Shrimps'
Ground: Mazuma Stadium, Christie Way, Westgate, Morecambe   LA4 4TB
Record Attendance: 9,324 (1962 – Christie Park)
Pitch Size: 110 × 73 yards

Colours: Red shirts with Red shorts
Telephone Nº: (01524) 411797
Fax Number: (01524) 832230
Ground Capacity: 6,476
Seating Capacity: 2,173
Web site: www.morecambefc.com
E-mail: office@morecambefc.com

GENERAL INFORMATION

Car Parking: Available at a school adjacent to the ground
Coach Parking: Available at the rear of the stadium
Nearest Railway Station: Morecambe Central (2 miles)
Nearest Bus Station: Morecambe
Club Shop: At the ground
Opening Times: Weekdays & Matchdays 9.00am to 5.00pm
Telephone Nº: (01524) 411797 Option 3

GROUND INFORMATION

Away Supporters' Entrances & Sections:
Dennison Trailers (East) Away Stand plus seating in part of the Main Stand.

ADMISSION INFO (2020/2021 PRICES)

Adult Standing: £18.00 – £19.00
Adult Seating: £23.00 – £28.00
Senior Citizen Standing: £15.00 – £16.00
Senior Citizen Seating: £19.00 – £28.00
Ages 18 to 22 Standing: £12.00
Ages 18 to 22 Seating: £17.00 – £28.00
Ages 11 to 17 Standing: £7.00
Ages 11 to 17 Seating: £8.00 – £28.00
Note: Under-11s are admitted free with a paying adult. Otherwise, the same prices as Ages 11 to 17 are charged. Tickets are £2.00 cheaper when purchased in advance
Programme Price: £3.00

FANS WITH DISABILITIES INFORMATION

Wheelchairs: Accommodated – 39 spaces available in total
Helpers: Admitted
Prices: Concessionary prices are charged for fans with disabilities. Helpers are admitted free of charge
Disabled Toilets: Available in all stands
Contact: (01524) 411797   (Bookings are preferred)

Travelling Supporters' Information:
Routes: Exit the M6 at Junction 34 and follow signs to Morecambe. Cross the River Lune via the Greyhound Bridge and continue, following signs for Morecambe onto the A589. At the first two roundabouts, keep in the right hand lane and carry straight on. Turn left at the third roundabout (Shrimp) and continue along Westgate for about a mile. Globe Stadium is on the right. Away fans car parking: Turn right after the Junior School towards Venture Caravan Park and the away car park is signposted.

NEWCASTLE UNITED FC

Founded: 1882 (**Entered League**: 1893)
Former Names: Newcastle East End FC (1882-1892)
amalgamated with Newcastle West End FC
Nickname: 'Magpies'
Ground: St. James Park, Strawberry Place,
Newcastle-Upon-Tyne   NE1 4ST
Ground Capacity: 52,354 (All seats)

Record Attendance: 68,386 (3rd September 1930)
Pitch Size: 115 × 74 yards
Colours: Black and White striped shirts, Black shorts
Telephone Nº: 0344 372-1892
Ticket Office: 0344 372-1892
Web Site: www.nufc.co.uk
E-mail: boxoffice@nufc.co.uk

GENERAL INFORMATION

Car Parking: Street parking
Coach Parking: By Police direction
Nearest Railway Station: Newcastle Central (¼ mile)
Nearest Bus Station: St. James' Boulevard (¼ mile)
Club Shop: At the ground
Opening Times: Monday to Saturday 9.00am – 5.00pm
Telephone Nº: 0344 372-1892

GROUND INFORMATION

Away Supporters' Entrances & Sections:
Rear of the Leazes Stand, entrance from Barrack Road
through turnstiles 91-94

ADMISSION INFO (2019/2020 PRICES)

Adult Seating: £27.00 – £64.00
Child Seating: £14.00 – £34.00 (in the Family Seating Area)
Senior Citizen Seating: £22.00 – £52.00
Please contact the club for 2019/2020 pricing information.
Programme Price: £3.00

FANS WITH DISABILITIES INFORMATION

Wheelchairs: 160 spaces in total in special areas
throughout the stadium   Lifts are available.
Helpers: One helper admitted per fan with disabilities
Prices: Half-price tickets for fans with disabilities. Helpers
are admitted free of charge
Disabled Toilets: Throughout the stadium (via Radar Key)
Commentaries are available for 20 blind supporters
Contact: (0191) 201-8457 or disabilitysupport@nufc.co.uk
Steve Storey (DLO)

Travelling Supporters' Information:
Routes: From the North: Follow the A1 into Newcastle, then follow Hexham signs into Percy Street. Turn right into Leazes Park Road; From the South: Take the A1M, then after Birtley Granada Services take the A1 Gateshead Western Bypass (bear left on the Motorway). Follow Airport signs for approximately 3 miles then take the A692 (Newcastle) sign, crossing the Redheugh Bridge. Proceed over three sets of traffic lights to the roundabout and take the 1st exit into Barrack Road; From the West: Take the A69 towards the City Centre. Pass Newcastle General Hospital. At the traffic lights after the Hospital turn left into Brighton Grove. After 70 yards turn right into Stanhope Street and proceed into Barrack Road for the ground.

NEWPORT COUNTY AFC

Founded: 1989   (**Entered League**: 2013)
Former Names: Newport AFC
Nickname: 'The Exiles'
Ground: Rodney Parade, Newport   NP19 0UU
Record Attendance: 9,836 (vs Tottenham Hotspur
in January 2018 when temporary seating was erected)
Pitch Size: 112 × 72 yards

Colours: Amber shirts with Black shorts
Telephone N°: (01633) 415376
Ticket Office: (01633) 264572
Ground Capacity: 7,850
Seating Capacity: 1,236
Web site: www.newport-county.co.uk
E-mail: office@newport-county.co.uk

GENERAL INFORMATION

Car Parking: Street parking only
Coach Parking: By Police direction
Nearest Railway Station: Newport (½ mile)
Nearest Bus Station: Newport
Club Shop: At Kingsway Shopping Centre, Newport
Opening Times: Monday to Saturday 9.30am to 5.00pm
(until 4.00pm on regular Saturdays). Saturday Matchdays
10.00am to 2.00pm.
Telephone N°: (01633) 264572

GROUND INFORMATION

Away Supporters' Entrances & Sections:
Sytner End turnstiles for Bisley Stand accommodation

ADMISSION INFO (2019/2020 PRICES)

Adult Standing: £20.00   **Adult Seating**: £22.00
Senior Citizen Standing/Seating: £18.00
Ages 16 to 21 Standing: £14.00   **Seating**: £16.00
Under-16s Standing/Seating: £10.00
Under-12s Standing/Seating: £8.00 (Under-6s free)
Note: Discounted prices are available for online purchases.
Prices for the 2020/2021 season were not available at the
time of going to press. Please contact the club for details.

FANS WITH DISABILITIES INFORMATION

Wheelchairs: Accommodated – 11 spaces available in total
Helpers: Admitted
Prices: Normal prices for fans with disabilities. Helpers free
Disabled Toilets: 4 available
Contact: (01633) 415376   (Bookings are not necessary)
Colin Faulkner (DLO) – equality@newport-county.co.uk

Travelling Supporters' Information:
Routes: From the West: Exit the M4 at Junction 26 of the M4 and take the 3rd exit at the roundabout onto Malpas Road. Take
the 2nd exit at the next roundabout then the 1st exit at the following roundabout across the River Usk bridge. * At the next set
of traffic lights bear right onto Chepstow Road, take the first right onto Cedar Road then the first right onto Corporation Road.
Take the next left onto Grafton Road and Rodney Parade is on left hand side; From The East: Exit the M4 at Junction 25A and
take the 1st exit at the roundabout onto Heidenheim Way. Take the 1st exit off the fly-over then the 2nd exit at the first roundabout then the 1st exit at the next roundabout across the River Usk bridge. Then as above *.

NORTHAMPTON TOWN FC

Founded: 1897 (**Entered League**: 1920)
Nickname: 'Cobblers'
Ground: PTS Academy Stadium, Upton Way,
Northampton NN5 5QA
Ground Capacity: 7,798 (All seats)
Record Attendance: 7,798 (September 2016)
Pitch Size: 116 × 72 yards

Colours: Claret and White shirts with White shorts
Telephone Nº: (01604) 683700
Ticket Office: (01604) 683777
Fax Number: (01604) 751613
Web Site: www.ntfc.co.uk
E-mail: wendy.lambell@ntfc.co.uk

GENERAL INFORMATION

Car Parking: At the ground
Coach Parking: At the ground
Nearest Railway Station: Northampton Castle (2 miles)
Nearest Bus Station: North Gate
Club Shop: At the ground
Opening Times: Monday to Friday 9.00am – 5.00pm..
Saturday Matchdays 11.00am to 5.00pm and non-match
Saturdays 9.00am to 12.00pm.
Telephone Nº: (01604) 683777

GROUND INFORMATION

Away Supporters' Entrances & Sections:
Moulton College Stand

ADMISSION INFO (2020/2021 PRICES)

Adult Seating: £24.00
Senior Citizen Seating: £20.00
Under-21s Seating: £18.00
Under-18s Seating: £12.00
Under-7s: Admitted free of charge
Note: Discounted prices are available for advance purchases

FANS WITH DISABILITIES INFORMATION

Wheelchairs: 55 spaces in total for Home and Away fans in
various areas of the ground
Helpers: One helper admitted per fan with disabilities
Prices: Normal prices for fans with disabilities. Helpers free
Disabled Toilets: Available
Commentaries are available for the blind
Contact: (01604) 683777 (Bookings are necessary) –
wendy.lambell@ntfc.co.uk (Supporters' Liaison Officer) –
07714 407448

Travelling Supporters' Information:
Routes: From All Parts: Exit the M1 at Junction 15A following the signs for Sixfields Leisure onto Upton Way – the ground is
approximately 2 miles.

NORWICH CITY FC

Founded: 1902 (**Entered League**: 1920)
Nickname: 'Canaries'
Ground: Carrow Road, Norwich   NR1 1JE
Ground Capacity: 27,244 (All seats)
Record Attendance: 43,984 (30th March 1963)
Pitch Size: 114 × 74 yards

Colours: Yellow shirts with Green shorts
Telephone Nº: (01603) 721902
Ticket Office: (01603) 721902 Option 1
Web Site: www.canaries.co.uk
E-mail: reception@canaries.co.uk

GENERAL INFORMATION

Car Parking: County Hall (NR1 2DW) and City Centre car parks are nearby
Coach Parking: Lower Clarence Road
Nearest Railway Station: Norwich Thorpe (1 mile)
Nearest Bus Station: Surrey Street, Norwich
Club Shop: At the ground and also stores in Chapelfield and the Castle Mall
Opening Times: Carrow Road store opens Monday to Saturday 9.00am to 5.30pm and Sunday 10.00am to 4.00pm. Chapelfield is open Monday to Saturday 9.00am to 6.00pm (until 8pm on Thursday and 7.00pm on Friday and Saturday), plus Sunday 11.00am to 5.00pm
Telephone Nº: (01603) 721902

GROUND INFORMATION

Away Supporters' Entrances & Sections:
South Stand using turnstiles 51-57

ADMISSION INFO (2020/2021 PRICES)

Adult Seating: £30.00
Senior Citizen Seating: £25.00
Under-18s Seating: £20.00
Under-12s Seating: £15.00
Programme Price: £3.00

FANS WITH DISABILITIES INFORMATION

Wheelchairs: 84 spaces for home fans and 13 for away fans in the South Stand. Plenty of spaces are also available for ambulant fans with disabilities
Helpers: One helper admitted per fan with disabilities
Prices: Normal prices for fans with disabilities. Helpers free
Disabled Toilets: Available – Radar key operated
Contact: (01603) 721902   (Bookings are necessary) – stephen.graham@canaries.co.uk (Supporters' Liaison Officer)

Travelling Supporters' Information:
Routes: From the South: Take the A11 or A140 and turn right onto the A47 towards Great Yarmouth & Lowestoft, take the A146 Norwich/Lowestoft sliproad, turn left towards Norwich and follow road signs for the Football Ground; From the West: Take the A47 on to the A146 Norwich/Lowestoft slip road. Turn left towards Norwich, follow the road signs for the Football Ground.

NOTTINGHAM FOREST FC

Founded: 1865 (**Entered League**: 1892)
Nickname: 'The Reds'
Ground: The City Ground, Nottingham   NG2 5FJ
Ground Capacity: 30,445 (All seats)
Record Attendance: 49,946 (28th October 1967)
Pitch Size: 112 × 76 yards

Colours: Red shirts with White shorts
Telephone Nº: (0115) 982-4444
Ticket Office: (0115) 982-4388
Web Site: www.nottinghamforest.co.uk
E-mail: reception@nottinghamforest.co.uk

GENERAL INFORMATION

Car Parking: Various nearby car parks and street parking
Coach Parking: Available at the stadium.
Nearest Railway Station: Nottingham Midland (½ mile)
Nearest Bus Station: Victoria Street/Broadmarsh Centre
Club Shop: At the ground
Opening Times: Weekdays 9.00am – 5.00pm; Matchdays 9.00am – kick-off and 30 minutes after the game; Sunday matchdays 10.00am – kick-off + 60 minutes after the game
Telephone Nº: (0115) 982-4305

GROUND INFORMATION

Away Supporters' Entrances & Sections:
Entrances via East car park for Bridgford Stand

ADMISSION INFO (2019/2020 PRICES)

Due to the introduction of a 'dynamic' pricing system, we suggest that fans contact the club for further details about admission prices for any particular game.
Programme Price: £3.00

FANS WITH DISABILITIES INFORMATION

Wheelchairs: 68 spaces in total for home fans around the ground plus 11 spaces for away fans in the Lower Bridgford Stand
Helpers: One helper admitted per fan with disabilities
Prices: Please contact the club for further information
Disabled Toilets: 7 available with radar key locks
Contact: (0115) 982-4391 or (0115) 982-4341 (Bookings are necessary) – Graham Murray (Safety and Security manager) – graham.murray@nottinghamforest.co.uk

Travelling Supporters' Information:
Routes: From the North: Exit the M1 at Junction 26 following Nottingham signs (A610) then signs to Melton Mowbray and Trent Bridge (A606). Cross the River Trent, turn left into Radcliffe Road then left again into Colwick Road for the ground; From the South: Exit the M1 at Junction 24 following signs for Nottingham (South) to Trent Bridge. Turn right into Radcliffe Road then left into Colwick Road; From the East: Take the A52 to West Bridgford and follow signs for Football & Cricket; From the West: Take the A52 into Nottingham, follow signs for Melton Mowbray and Trent Bridge, cross the River Trent (then as North).

OLDHAM ATHLETIC FC

Founded: 1895 (**Entered League**: 1907)
Former Names: Pine Villa FC (1895-1899)
Nickname: 'Latics'
Ground: Boundary Park, Furtherwood Road, Oldham   OL1 2PA
Ground Capacity: 13,513 (All seats)
Record Attendance: 47,671 (25th January 1930)

Pitch Size: 110 × 72 yards
Colours: Blue shirts, shorts and socks
Telephone Nº: (0161) 624-4972
Ticket Office: (0161) 785-5150
Fax Number: (0161) 627-5915
Web Site: www.oldhamathletic.co.uk
E-mail: enquiries@oldhamathletic.co.uk

GENERAL INFORMATION

Car Parking: 350 spaces in North Stand car park (permit holders only) and also the nearby Hospital car park (£5.00)
Coach Parking: At the ground
Nearest Railway Station: Oldham Werneth (1½ miles)
Nearest Bus Station: Oldham Town Centre (2 miles)
Club Shop: In the North Stand
Opening Times: Tuesday to Saturday 10.00am to 3.00pm.
Telephone Nº: (0161) 624-4972

GROUND INFORMATION

Away Supporters' Entrances & Sections:
Chadderton Road Stand

ADMISSION INFO (2020/2021 PRICES)

Adult Seating: £22.00
Concessionary Seating: £10.00
Under-18s Seating: £7.00
Under-12s Seating: £5.00
Note: Discounts are available for tickets in the Family Stand in addition to those purchased in advance.
Programme Price: £3.00

FANS WITH DISABILITIES INFORMATION

Wheelchairs: 60 spaces in the special areas in the North Stand, Chadderton Road Stand and Rochdale Road Stand
Helpers: One helper admitted per fan with disabilities if on the higher/enhanced rate of care
Prices: Normal prices for fans with disabilities. Helpers free
Disabled Toilets: Available in the North Stand, Rochdale Road Stand and the Chadderton Road Stand
Contact: (0161) 785-5179 (Bookings are necessary) Natalie Atkinson (DLO) – 07979 187090 or e-mail natalie.atkinson@oildhamathletic.co.uk

Travelling Supporters' Information:
Routes: From All Parts: Exit the M62 at Junction 20 and take the A627M to the junction with the A664. Take the 1st exit at the roundabout onto Broadway, then the 1st right into Hilbre Avenue which leads to the car park at the ground.

OXFORD UNITED FC

Founded: 1893 (**Re-Entered League**: 2010)
Former Names: Headington United FC (1893-1960)
Nickname: 'U's'
Ground: Kassam Stadium, Grenoble Road, Oxford, OX4 4XP
Ground Capacity: 12,500 (All seats)

Record Attendance: 22,750 (At the Manor Ground)
Pitch Size: 110 × 70 yards
Colours: Yellow shirts with Navy Blue shorts
Telephone Nº: (01865) 337500
Ticket Office: (01865) 337533
Web Site: www.oufc.co.uk

GENERAL INFORMATION

Car Parking: 2,000 free spaces available at the ground
Coach Parking: At the ground
Nearest Railway Station: Oxford (4 miles)
Nearest Bus Station: Oxford
Club Shop: At the ground and also in the Covered Market in Oxford city centre
Opening Times: Monday to Friday 10.00am to 5.00pm and Matchdays from 10.00am until kick-off at the ground. The Covered Market shop opens Tuesday to Friday 9.00am to 5.00pm and Saturday 10.00am to 4.00pm.
Telephone Nº: (01865) 747231 (at the ground)

GROUND INFORMATION

Away Supporters' Entrances & Sections:
North Stand turnstiles for North Stand accommodation.
Ticket office for away supporters is adjacent

ADMISSION INFO (2019/2020 PRICES)

Adult Seating: £20.00 – £28.00
Under-21s Seating: £14.00 – £20.00
Under-18s Seating: £8.00 – £18.00
Under-13s Seating: £6.00 – £15.00
Under-7s Seating: Free with a paying adult in the Family Area. Otherwise £4.00 – £12.00
Senior Citizen Seating: £13.00 – £21.00
Programme Price: £3.00

FANS WITH DISABILITIES INFORMATION

Wheelchairs: Accommodated in areas in the North, East and South Stands
Helpers: One assistant admitted per fan with disabilities
Prices: Normal prices for fans with disabilities. One assistant also admitted free of charge if required
Disabled Toilets: Available throughout the ground
Contact: (01865) 337533   (Bookings are not necessary)
Kath Faulkner (DLO) – kfaulkner@oufc.co.uk (07966 016549)

Travelling Supporters' Information:
Routes: From the Oxford Ring Road take the A4074 towards Henley and Reading then turn left after ½ mile following signs for the Oxford Science Park. Bear left and go straight on at two roundabouts then the Stadium is on the left in Grenoble Road. The Kassam Stadium is clearly signposted on all major roads in Oxford.

PETERBOROUGH UNITED FC

Founded: 1934 (**Entered League**: 1960)
Nickname: 'Posh'
Ground: The Weston Homes Stadium, London Road, Peterborough   PE2 8AL
Ground Capacity: 15,314
Seating Capacity: 10,000
Pitch Size: 112 × 71 yards

Record Attendance: 30,096 (20th February 1965)
Colours: Cobalt Blue shirts with Blue shorts
Telephone Nº: (01733) 563947
Ticket Office: 0844 847-1934
Fax Number: (01733) 344140
Web Site: www.theposh.com
E-mail: info@theposh.com

GENERAL INFORMATION

Car Parking: Adjacent to the ground at the Pleasure Fair Meadow council car park and the Railworld car park.
Coach Parking: In front of the (North) Main Stand
Nearest Railway Station: Peterborough (1 mile)
Nearest Bus Station: Peterborough (1 mile)
Club Shop: At the ground
Opening Times: Tuesday to Friday 9.00am to 5.00pm (from 10.00am on Mondays). Saturday Matchdays 10.00pm to 3.00pm then 5.00pm to 5.30pm
Telephone Nº: (01733) 865668

GROUND INFORMATION

Away Supporters' Entrances & Sections:
Blocks 'A' and 'B' of the North Stand

ADMISSION INFO (2019/2020 PRICES)

Adult Standing: £22.00 – £24.00
Adult Seating: £26.00 – £28.00
Senior Citizen Standing: £17.00 – £19.00
Senior Citizen Seating: £21.00 – £23.00
Under-22s Standing: £13.00 – £15.00
Under-22s Seating: £17.00 – £19.00
Ages 12 to 17 Standing/Seating: £9.00 – £11.00
Under-12s Standing/Seating: £5.00
Note: Prices vary depending on the category of the game. Discounts are available for tickets purchased in advance
Programme Price: £3.00

FANS WITH DISABILITIES INFORMATION

Wheelchairs: 57 spaces available in total in the South Stand, North Stand and Motorpoint Stand
Helpers: One helper admitted per fan with disabilities
Prices: Normal prices for fans with disabilities. Helpers free
Disabled Toilets: Available in all areas of the ground
Contact: (01733) 865674 Option 2 (Bookings are necessary) Chris Abbott – fans@theposh.com

Travelling Supporters' Information:
Routes: From the North and West: Take the A1 then the A47 into the Town Centre and follow Whittlesey signs across the river into London Road; From the East: Take the A47 into the Town Centre (then as from the North); From the South: Take the A1 then the A15 into London Road.

PLYMOUTH ARGYLE FC

Founded: 1886 (**Entered League**: 1920)
Former Names: Argyle FC (1886-1903)
Nickname: 'Pilgrims' 'Argyle'
Ground: Home Park, Plymouth PL2 3DQ
Ground Capacity: 17,904 (All seats)
Record Attendance: 43,596 (10th October 1936)
Pitch Size: 112 × 73 yards

Colours: Green shirts and White shorts
Telephone Nº: (01752) 562561
Ticket Office: (01752) 907700
Fax Number: (01752) 606167
Web Site: www.pafc.co.uk
E-mail: argyle@pafc.co.uk

GENERAL INFORMATION

Car Parking: Car park for 1,000 cars is adjacent
Coach Parking: Central Park Car Park
Nearest Railway Station: Plymouth North Road
Nearest Bus Station: Coach hub off Mayflower Street
Club Shop: At the ground
Opening Times: Monday to Friday 9.00am to 5.00pm,
Saturday home matchdays 9.00am to 3.00pm plus 30
minutes after the game. Saturday away matchdays 10.00am
to 1.00pm.
Telephone Nº: (01752) 562561

GROUND INFORMATION

Away Supporters' Entrances & Sections:
Barn Park End turnstiles for Blocks 22/23 (covered seating)

ADMISSION INFO (2019/2020 PRICES)

Adult Seating: £23.00
Under-18s Seating: £10.00
Under-12s Seating: £6.00   **Under-8s Seating**: £4.00
Senior Citizen/Under-23s Seating: £18.00
Note: Tickets are cheaper if purchased before the matchday
and Family Tickets are also available.
Programme Price: £3.00

FANS WITH DISABILITIES INFORMATION

Wheelchairs: 80 spaces Home fans and 28 spaces for Away
fans at pitch level
Helpers: One helper admitted per fan with disabilities
Prices: Normal prices apply for fans with disabilities.
Helpers are admitted free of charge
Disabled Toilets: Available throughout the stadium
Commentaries are available for the visually impaired
Contact: 0773 7002-262   nikki.francis@pafc.co.uk –
Disability Liaison Officer   (Bookings are necessary)

Travelling Supporters' Information:
Routes: From All Parts: Take the A38 to Tavistock Road (A386), then branch left following signs for Home Park (A386) and
continue for 1¼ miles. The car park for the ground is on the left (signposted Home Park).

PORTSMOUTH FC

Founded: 1898 (**Entered League**: 1920)
Nickname: 'Pompey'
Ground: Fratton Park, 57 Frogmore Road,
Portsmouth, Hants   PO4 8RA
Ground Capacity: 19,669 (All seats)
Record Attendance: 51,385 (26th February 1949)
Pitch Size: 110 × 71 yards

Colours: Blue shirts with White shorts
Telephone N°: 0345 646-1898
Ticket Office: 0345 646-1898
Fax Number: (023) 9273-4129
Web Site: www.portsmouthfc.co.uk
E-mail: info@pompeyfc.co.uk

GENERAL INFORMATION

Car Parking: Street parking plus a limited number of spaces at Fratton Park (first come, first served – £10.00 charge)
Coach Parking: By Police direction
Nearest Railway Station: Fratton (adjacent)
Nearest Bus Station: The Hard, Portsmouth
Club Shop: At the ground in Anson Road (North Stand)
Opening Times: Monday to Friday 9.00am – 5.30pm. Saturday and Weekday Matchdays 9.00am until half-time.
Telephone N°: (023) 9421-1270

GROUND INFORMATION

Away Supporters' Entrances & Sections:
Apsley Road – Milton Road side for Apsley Road End

ADMISSION INFO (2019/2020 PRICES)

Adult Seating: £26.00
Junior Seating: £10.00 (£5.00 when accompanied)
Senior Citizen Seating: £20.00 (Ages 65+)
Ages 18 to 22 Seating: £18.00
Ages 2 to 17 Seating: £8.00
Note: Adults, Senior Citizens or Ages 17 to 22 must be accompanied by a Junior if they sit in the Family Section.
Programme Price: £3.00

FANS WITH DISABILITIES INFORMATION

Wheelchairs: 58 spaces available in total in a special section in the Fratton End including 5 spaces for away fans
Helpers: One helper admitted per fan with disabilities
Prices: Wheelchair users are charged £15.00 and ambulant fans with disabilities are charged £16.00. Free for helpers
Disabled Toilets: One available in disabled section (Radar Key required for access)
Contact: 0345 646-1898 (Bookings are necessary) – courtneyhollier@pompeyfc.co.uk (Disability Liaison Officer)

Travelling Supporters' Information:
Routes: From the North and West: Take the M27 and M275 to the end then take the 2nd exit at the roundabout and after ¼ mile turn right at the 'T' junction into London Road (A2047). After 1¼ miles cross the railway bridge and turn left into Goldsmith Avenue. After ½ mile turn left into Frogmore Road; From the East: Take the A27 following Southsea signs (A2030). Turn left at the roundabout (3 miles) onto the A288, then right into Priory Crescent and next right into Carisbrooke Road for the ground.

PORT VALE FC

Founded: 1876 (**Entered League**: 1892)
Former Names: Burslem Port Vale FC
Nickname: 'Valiants'
Ground: Vale Park, Hamil Road, Burslem,
Stoke-on-Trent ST6 1AW
Ground Capacity: 19,052 (All seats)
Record Attendance: 49,768 (20th February 1960)
Pitch Size: 114 × 77 yards

Colours: White shirts with Black detail, Black shorts
Telephone Nº: (01782) 655800
Ticket Office: (01782) 655821
Fax Number: (01782) 834981
Web Site: www.port-vale.co.uk
E-mail: enquiries@port-vale.co.uk

GENERAL INFORMATION

Car Parking: Car parks at the ground (£5.00)
Coach Parking: Hamil Road car park (£25.00)
Nearest Railway Station: Stoke
Nearest Bus Station: Burslem (adjacent)
Club Shop: At the ground
Opening Times: Monday to Friday 9.00am – 5.00pm and
Saturday Matchdays 9.30am to 3.15pm
Telephone Nº: (01782) 655822

GROUND INFORMATION

Away Supporters' Entrances & Sections:
Hamil Road turnstiles, numbers 1 to 8

ADMISSION INFO (2020/2021 PRICES)

Adult Seating: £20.00 – £21.00
Ages 12 to 17 Seating: £8.00
Ages 18 to 21 Seating: £15.00 – £16.00
Under-12s Seating: Free of charge
Concessionary Seating: £15.00 – £16.00
Note: Discounted Family Tickets are available
Programme Price: £3.00

FANS WITH DISABILITIES INFORMATION

Wheelchairs: 46 spaces available in a special area in the
Lorne Street/Bycars Corner
Helpers: One helper admitted per fan with disabilities
Prices: Normal prices for fans with disabilities. Helpers free
Disabled Toilets: Available
Commentaries are available – please contact the club
Contact: (01782) 655821   (Bookings are necessary) –
janet.ellis@port-vale.co.uk (Disability Liaison Officer)

Travelling Supporters' Information:
Routes: From the North: Exit the M6 at Junction 16 and follow Stoke signs (A500). Branch left off the A500 at the exit signposted
Tunstall and take the 2nd exit at the roundabout into Newcastle Street. Proceed through the traffic lights into Moorland Road
and take the 2nd turning on the left into Hamil Road; From the South and West: Exit the M6 at Junction 15 and take the A5006
and A500. After 6¼ miles branch left (then as from the North); From the East: Take the A50 or A52 into Stoke following Burslem
signs into Waterloo Road, turn right at Burslem crossroads into Moorland Road (then as from the North).

PRESTON NORTH END FC

Founded: 1880 (**Entered League**: 1888)
Nickname: 'Lilywhites' 'North End'
Ground: Deepdale, Sir Tom Finney Way, Preston, PR1 6RU
Ground Capacity: 23,404 (All seats)
Record Attendance: 42,684 (23rd April 1938)
Pitch Size: 109 × 73 yards   (100 × 67 metres)

Colours: White shirts with Blue shorts
Telephone N°: 0344 856-1964
Ticket Office: 0344 856-1966
Web Site: www.pnefc.net
E-mail: enquiries@pne.com

GENERAL INFORMATION

Car Parking: Four official car parks at the stadium plus further parking at Moor Park School
Coach Parking: By prior arrangement with the club
Nearest Railway Station: Preston (2 miles)
Nearest Bus Station: Preston (1 mile)
Club Shop: At the ground
Opening Times: Monday to Saturday 9.00am to 5.00pm and midweek matchdays 9.00am until kick-off
Telephone N°: 0344 856-1965

GROUND INFORMATION

Away Supporters' Entrances & Sections:
Bill Shankly Kop

ADMISSION INFO (2019/2020 PRICES)

Adult Seating: £26.00 – £32.00
Age 19 to 24/Student/Apprentice Seating: £16.00 – £23.00
Ages 11 to 18 Seating: £9.00 – £10.00
Under-11s Seating: £2.00
Senior Citizen Seating: £18.00 – £25.00
Note: Discounted Family Tickets are also available
Programme Price: £3.00

FANS WITH DISABILITIES INFORMATION

Wheelchairs: 160 spaces are available for advance order
Helpers: One helper admitted per fan with disabilities
Prices: Normal prices for fans with disabilities. Helpers free
Disabled Toilets: Available throughout the ground
Commentaries are available for the blind
Contact: (01772) 693324 (Bookings are usually necessary)
Hannah Woodburn (DLO) – hannah@pne.com (07787 275842)

Travelling Supporters' Information:
Routes: From the North: Take the M6 then the M55 to Junction 1. Follow signs for Preston (A6). After 2 miles turn left at the crossroads into Blackpool Road (A5085). Turn right ¾ mile into Deepdale; From the South and East: Exit the M6 at Junction 31 and follow Preston signs (A59). Take the 2nd exit at the roundabout (1 mile) into Blackpool Road. Turn left after 1¼ miles into Deepdale; From the West: Exit the M55 at Junction 1 (then as from the North).

QUEEN'S PARK RANGERS FC

Founded: 1882 (**Entered League**: 1920)
Former Names: Formed by the amalgamation of St. Jude's FC and Christchurch Rangers FC
Nickname: 'Rangers' 'R's'
Ground: The Kiyan Prince Foundation Stadium, South Africa Road, London W12 7PJ
Ground Capacity: 18,181 (All seats)

Record Attendance: 35,353 (27th April 1974)
Pitch Size: 109 × 72 yards
Colours: Blue and White hooped shirts, White shorts
Telephone N°: (020) 8743-0262
Ticket Office: 08444 777007
Web Site: www.qpr.co.uk
E-mail: boxoffice@qpr.co.uk

GENERAL INFORMATION

Car Parking: Street parking
Coach Parking: By Police direction
Nearest Railway Station: Shepherd's Bush
Nearest Tube Station: White City (Central) or Wood Lane (Hammersmith & City)
Club Shop: Superstore at the ground
Opening Times: Weekdays 9.00am to 5.00pm. Weekday matchdays until 15 minutes before kick-off. Non-match Saturdays 9.00am to 5.00pm. Saturday matchdays 9.00am until 15 minutes before kick-off then 45 minutes after game (but not for evening matches)
Telephone N°: (020) 8749-6862

GROUND INFORMATION

Away Supporters' Entrances & Sections:
Access via South Africa Road turnstile 2 for School End Lower and Ellerslie Road turnstile 13 for School End Upper

ADMISSION INFO (2019/2020 PRICES)

Adult Seating: £19.00 – £39.00
Senior Citizen/Ages 18 to 21 Seating: £13.00 – £29.00
Under-18s Seating: £9.00 – £22.00
Under-8s Seating (Accompanied): Free – £19.00
Note: Prices shown are for matchday ticket purchases. Discounts are available to members and for advance purchases
Programme Price: £3.50

FANS WITH DISABILITIES INFORMATION

Wheelchairs: 24 spaces available
Helpers: One helper admitted per wheelchair
Prices: Concessionary prices for fans with disabilities. Free of charge for helpers
Disabled Toilets: Available
Commentaries for the blind are available in the Ellerslie Road Stand. Please contact the Ticket Office to arrange this facility.
Contact: (020) 8740-2502 (Bookings are necessary)
Joshua Scott (DLO) - joshua.scott@qpr.co.uk 07880 204344

Travelling Supporters' Information:
Routes: From the North: Take M1 & M406 North Circular for Neasden, go left after ¾ mile (A404) following signs for Harlesden, Hammersmith, past White City Stadium, right into White City Road and left into South Africa Road; From the South: Take A206 then A3 across Putney Bridge and follow signs to Hammersmith then Oxford (A219) to Shepherd's Bush. Join the A4020 following signs to Acton, turn right (¼ mile) into Loftus Road; From the East: Take the A12, A406 then the A503 to join the Ring Road, follow Oxford signs and join the A40(M), branch left (2 miles) to the M41, take the 3rd exit at the roundabout to the A4020 (then as South); From the West: Take the M4 to Chiswick then the A315 & A402 to Shepherd's Bush, join A4020 (then as South).

READING FC

Founded: 1871 (**Entered League:** 1920)
Former Names: Formed by the amalgamation of Hornets FC (1877) and Earley FC (1889)
Nickname: 'Royals'
Ground: Madejski Stadium, Junction 11 M4, Reading, Berkshire RG2 0FL
Ground Capacity: 24,161 (All seats)
Record Attendance: 24,184 (vs Everton, 17/11/12)

Pitch Size: 114 × 74 yards
Colours: Blue and White hooped shirts, White shorts
Telephone N°: (0118) 968-1100
Ticket Office: (0118) 968-1313
Fax Number: (0118) 968-1101
Web Site: www.readingfc.co.uk
E-mail: supporterservices@readingfc.co.uk

GENERAL INFORMATION
Car Parking: 1,800 spaces available at the ground (£10.00). Also another 2,000 spaces available nearby
Coach Parking: Please contact the club for details
Nearest Railway Station: Reading Central
Nearest Bus Station: Reading
Club Shop: At the ground
Opening Times: Monday to Saturday 9.00am – 5.30pm
Telephone N°: (0118) 968-1234

GROUND INFORMATION
Away Supporters' Entrances & Sections:
Turnstiles 9 and 10 for South Stand accommodation

ADMISSION INFO (2019/2020 PRICES)
Adult Seating: £23.00 – £29.00
Over-65s Seating: £16.00 – £20.00
Ages 18 to 24 Seating: £13.00 – £16.00
Under-18s Seating: £8.00 – £13.00
Under-13s Seating: £5.00 – £10.00
Note: Prices shown are for matchday ticket purchases. Discounts are available to members and for advance purchases
Programme Price: £3.00

FANS WITH DISABILITIES INFORMATION
Wheelchairs: 73 spaces are available for home fans and 14 spaces are available for away fans throughout the stadium
Prices: Normal prices apply for fans with disabilities. Helpers are admitted free of charge
Disabled Toilets: Available
Commentaries for approximately 12 people are available
Contact: (0118) 968-1313 Option 2 (Bookings necessary)
Jessica Hammant-Cracknell – disability@readingfc.co.uk

Travelling Supporters' Information:
Routes: The stadium is situated just off Junction 11 of the M4 near Reading.

ROCHDALE AFC

Founded: 1907 (**Entered League**: 1921)
Former Names: Rochdale Town FC
Nickname: 'The Dale'
Ground: The Crown Oil Arena, Rochdale   OL11 5DR
Ground Capacity: 10,249
Seating Capacity: 7,913
Record Attendance: 24,231 (10th December 1949)

Pitch Size: 114 × 76 yards
Colours: Blue and Black striped shirts with Blue shorts
Telephone Nº: (01706) 644648
Ticket Office: (01706) 644648 Option 8
Web Site: www.rochdaleafc.co.uk
E-mail: office@rochdaleafc.co.uk

GENERAL INFORMATION
Car Parking: Street parking only
Coach Parking: By Police direction
Nearest Railway Station: Rochdale (2 miles)
Nearest Bus Station: Town Centre (1 mile)
Club Shop: At the ground
Opening Times: Weekdays 9.00am to 5.00pm, Saturday matchdays from 9.00am to 3.00pm then open again after the final whistle. Other Saturdays from 9.00am to 12.00pm
Telephone Nº: (01706) 644648 Option 3

GROUND INFORMATION
Away Supporters' Entrances & Sections:
Turnstiles 11 to 18 for Willbutts Lane

ADMISSION INFO (2019/2020 PRICES)
Adult Standing: £20.00
Adult Seating: £23.00 – £25.00
Ages 16 to 21/Senior Citizen Standing: £15.00
Ages 16 to 21/Senior Citizen Seating: £17.00 – £19.00
Under-16s Standing/Seating: £8.00
Note: Certain tickets are cheaper if purchased in advance.
Programme Price: £3.00

FANS WITH DISABILITIES INFORMATION
Wheelchairs: 33 spaces in total in special sections in the Main, Pearl Street and Willbutts Lane Stands
Helpers: One helper admitted per fan with disabilities
Prices: Concessionary prices are charged for wheelchair users. Ambulant fans with disabilities pay normal prices. Helpers are admitted free of charge
Disabled Toilets: Available
Contact: Nicola Toolan (DLO) – 07706 753594
nicola.toolan@rochdaleafc.co.uk

Travelling Supporters' Information:
Routes: From All Parts: Exit the M62 at Junction 20 and take the A627(M) signposted Rochdale. At the end of this link road, filter left carry on for 400 yards and go straight on at the roundabout into Roche Valley Way signposted Spotland Stadium. At the traffic lights go staight ahead and the ground is on the right after ½ mile.

ROTHERHAM UNITED FC

Founded: 1870 (**Entered League**: 1893)
Former Names: Rotherham Town FC (1870-1896), Thornhill United FC (1884-1905) and Rotherham County FC (1905-1925)
Nickname: 'The Millers'
Ground: AESSEAL New York Stadium, New York Way, Rotherham S60 1AH
Ground Capacity: 12,000 (All seats)

Pitch Size: 110 × 72 yards
Record Attendance: 11,758 (7th September 2013)
Colours: Red shirts with White sleeves, White shorts
Telephone Nº: (01709) 827760
Ticket Office: (01709) 827768
Fax Number: (01709) 827774
Web Site: www.themillers.co.uk
E-mail: office@rotherhamunited.net

GENERAL INFORMATION

Car Parking: Street Parking and in Sheffield Road car parks
Coach Parking: At the stadium by arrangement (£25.00)
Nearest Railway Station: Rotherham Central (½ mile)
Nearest Bus Station: Rotherham Town Centre (½ mile)
Club Shop: At the ground
Opening Times: Weekdays 9.00am to 5.00pm, Saturdays 9.00am to 1.00pm (Matchdays until 30 minutes after kick-off)
Telephone Nº: (01709) 827768

GROUND INFORMATION

Away Supporters' Entrances & Sections:
Meditemp Stand

ADMISSION INFO (2020/2021 PRICES)

Adult Seating: £25.00 – £29.00
Senior Citizen/Student Seating: £15.00 – £19.00
Under-18s Seating: £9.00 – £11.00
Under-13s Seating: £7.00 – £9.00
Under-8s Seating: £2.00 in the Family Stand
Programme Price: £3.00

FANS WITH DISABILITIES INFORMATION

Wheelchairs: Accommodated
Helpers: One helper admitted with each fan with disabilities
Prices: Supporters with disabilities are charged concessionary prices. Helpers are admitted free of charge
Disabled Toilets: Available
Contact: (01709) 827768 (Bookings are necessary) John Bird (DLO) – dlo@rotherhamunited.net

Travelling Supporters' Information:
Routes: From the North: Exit the M1 at Junction 34, follow Rotherham (A6109) signs to the traffic lights and turn right. The ground is ¼ mile on the right; From the South & West: Exit the M1 at Junction 33, turn right and follow signs for Rotherham. Turn left at the roundabout then right at the next roundabout. Follow the dual carriageway and continue straight on at the next roundabout. Turn left at the following roundabout and the ground is on the left after ¼ mile; From the East: Take the A630 into Rotherham following Sheffield signs. Turn left at the 3rd roundabout (signposted Masborough) and the ground is on the right.

SALFORD CITY FC

Photo courtesy of John Mills @ Altius Photography

Founded: 1940 (**Entered League**: 2019)
Former Names: Salford Central FC, Salford FC, Salford Amateurs FC plus some other early names
Nickname: 'The Ammies'
Ground: The Peninsula Stadium, Moor Lane, Salford, Manchester   M7 3PZ
Record Attendance: 4,518 (vs Leeds United, 13/8/19)

Colours: Red shirts with White shorts
Telephone Nº: (0161) 241-9772
Ground Capacity: 5,106
Seating Capacity: 2,246
Pitch Size: 110 × 70 yards
Web site: www.salfordcityfc.co.uk
E-mail: enquiries@salfordcityfc.co.uk

GENERAL INFORMATION

Car Parking: Street parking plus Park and Ride from Agecroft Industrial Estate (M27 8SJ) – £2.00 charge
Coach Parking: At the ground
Nearest Railway Station: Clifton (2½ miles)
Nearest Bus Station: Services 93, 97 and 98 stop outside the ground
Club Shop: At the ground
Opening Times: Matchdays only
Telephone Nº: ()161) 241-9772

GROUND INFORMATION

Away Supporters' Entrances & Sections:
East Stand Turnstiles Block A

ADMISSION INFO (2019/2020 PRICES)

Adult Standing: £10.00
Adult Seating: £10.00
Senior Citizen/Junior Standing: £5.00
Senior Citizen/Junior Seating: £5.00
Note: Under-5s are admitted free of charge when attending the game with a paying adult.

FANS WITH DISABILITIES INFORMATION

Wheelchairs: Accommodated
Helpers: Admitted
Prices: Normal prices are charged for fans with disabilities. Helpers are admitted free of charge
Disabled Toilets: Available in the club house
Contact: (0161) 241-9772   (Bookings are not necessary) – andy.giblin@salfordcityfc.co.uk (Secretary – 07808 254646)

Travelling Supporters' Information:
Routes: Exit the M60 at Junction 17 and take the A56 Bury New Road towards Prestwich. Continue along, passing the A6044 (Hilton Lane) road then turn right along Moor Lane heading towards Kersal Moor and the Golf Course. The ground is on the left hand side of the road after a few hundred yards.

SCUNTHORPE UNITED FC

Founded: 1899 (**Entered League**: 1950)
Former Name: Scunthorpe and Lindsey United FC (1899-1912)
Nickname: 'The Iron'
Ground: The Sands Venue Stadium, Glanford Park, Jack Brownsword Way, Scunthorpe   DN15 8TD
Ground Capacity: 9,088
Seating Capacity: 6,322

Record Attendance: 9,077 (22nd September 2010)
Pitch Size: 112 × 72 yards
Colours: Blue shirt with Claret trim, Blue shorts
Telephone Nº: (01724) 840139
Ticket Office: (01724) 747670 (www.sufctickets.com)
Fax Number: (01724) 857986
Web Site: www.scunthorpe-united.co.uk
E-mail: receptionist@scunthorpe-united.co.uk

GENERAL INFORMATION

Car Parking: Spaces for 600 cars at the ground (£3.00)
Coach Parking: At the ground
Nearest Railway Station: Scunthorpe (1½ miles)
Nearest Bus Station: Scunthorpe (1½ miles)
Club Shop: At the ground
Opening Times: Weekdays 8.30am to 5.00pm
Matchdays 9.00am to 3.00pm and 4.45pm to 5.15pm
Telephone Nº: (01724) 849344

GROUND INFORMATION

Away Supporters' Entrances & Sections:
Turnstiles 6-7 for the South Stand (AMS Stand)

ADMISSION INFO (2019/2020 PRICES)

Adult Standing: £21.00 – £22.00
Adult Seating: £23.00 – £26.00
Concessionary Standing: £15.00 – £16.00
Concessionary Seating: £16.00 – £18.00
Under-18s Standing: £8.00 – £9.00   (Under-12s free)
Under-18s Seating: £6.00 – £9.00
Note: Discounted prices are available for members
Programme Price: £3.00

FANS WITH DISABILITIES INFORMATION

Wheelchairs: 10 spaces for Home fans and 6 spaces for Away fans in designated section of the Clugston Stand
Helpers: One helper admitted per fan with disabilities
Prices: Normal prices for fans with disabilities. One helper admitted free per fan requiring medium to higher rate of care.
Disabled Toilets: Available
Commentaries are available for the blind
Contact: (01724) 747683   (Bookings are necessary)
Pete Wallace (DLO) – pete.wallace@scunthorpe-united.co.uk

Travelling Supporters' Information:
Routes: From All Parts: Exit the M180 at Junction 3 onto the M181. Follow the M181 to the roundabout with the A18 and take the A18 towards Scunthorpe – the ground is on the right after 200 yards.

SHEFFIELD UNITED FC

Founded: 1889 (**Entered League**: 1892)
Nickname: 'Blades'
Ground: Bramall Lane, Sheffield   S2 4SU
Ground Capacity: 32,125 (All seats)
Record Attendance: 68,287 (15th February 1936)
Pitch Size: 110 × 73 yards

Colours: Red and White striped shirts, Black shorts
Telephone Nº: (0114) 253-7200
Ticket Office: (0114) 253-7200
Web Site: www.sufc.co.uk
E-mail: info@sufc.co.uk

GENERAL INFORMATION

Car Parking: Street parking only
Coach Parking: By Police direction
Nearest Railway Station: Sheffield Midland (1 mile)
Nearest Bus Station: Pond Street, Sheffield (1 mile)
Club Shop: At the ground
Opening Times: Monday to Friday 9.00am to 5.00pm (until kick-off on matchdays). Saturdays 9.00am to 4.00pm (until 3.00pm and then for 30 minutes after the game on matchdays)
Telephone Nº: (0114) 253-7200

GROUND INFORMATION

Away Supporters' Entrances & Sections:
Redbrik – Bramall Lane Stand Lower Tier

ADMISSION INFO (2019/2020 PRICES)

Adult Seating: £29.00 – £45.00
Senior Citizen Seating: £22.00 – £36.00
Under-22s/Student Seating: £19.00 – £29.00
Under-18s Seating: £13.00 – £23.00
Junior Seating: £11.00 – £21.00
Programme Price: £3.00

FANS WITH DISABILITIES INFORMATION

Wheelchairs: 95 spaces available for home fans along with 10 spaces for away fans in the Westfield Corner Stand
Helpers: One helper admitted per wheelchair
Prices: Concessionary prices for fans with disabilities. Free of charge for helpers
Disabled Toilets: 12 available within the enclosure
Commentaries available for the blind on request
Contact: (0114) 253-7200   (Bookings are necessary) – kay.adkins@sufc.co.uk (Disability Liaison Officer)

Travelling Supporters' Information:
Routes: From the North: Exit the M1 at Junction 33 following signs to Sheffield (A57) and continue along Sheffield Parkway until the Park Square roundabout. Take the 3rd exit and follow the A61 (Sheffield). Midland Station is on the left, the road veers to the left then take the middle lane following the ring road to the right. Take the first exit at the roundabout into Bramhall Lane.; From the South: Exit the M1 at junction 29 and take the A617 (Chesterfield). Take the 3rd exit at the roundabout onto the A61 and continue to the Earl of Arundel and Surrey Public House. Turn left and continue into Bramhall Lane; From the East: Exit the M1 at Junctions 31 or 33 and take the A57 to the roundabout, take the 3rd exit into Sheaf Street (then as from the North); From the West: Take the A57 into Sheffield and take the 4th exit at the roundabout into Upper Hanover Street and at the 2nd roundabout take the 3rd exit into Bramall Lane.

SHEFFIELD WEDNESDAY FC

Founded: 1867 (**Entered League**: 1892)
Former Name: The Wednesday FC
Nickname: 'Owls'
Ground: Hillsborough, Sheffield S6 1SW
Ground Capacity: 34,835 (All seats)
Record Attendance: 72,841 (17th February 1934)

Pitch Size: 116 × 75 yards
Colours: Blue and White striped shirts, Black shorts
Telephone Nº: 03700 20-1867
Ticket Hotline: 03700 20-1867 Option 1
Web Site: www.swfc.co.uk
E-mail: mediaenquiries@swfc.co.uk

GENERAL INFORMATION

Car Parking: Street parking plus private car parks around the stadium
Coach Parking: Clay Wheels Lane
Nearest Railway Station: Sheffield Midland (4 miles)
Nearest Bus Station: Pond Street, Sheffield (4 miles)
Club Shop: At the ground
Ground Opening Times: Monday to Friday from 9.00am to 5.00pm and non-match Saturdays from 9.00am to 12.00pm. Saturdays matchdays 9.00am to 3.00pm then 45 minutes after the game.
Telephone Nº: 03700 20-1867

GROUND INFORMATION

Away Supporters' Entrances & Sections:
Leppings Lane turnstiles for the West Stand, Upper Tier

ADMISSION INFO (2019/2020 PRICES)

Adult Seating: £25.00 – £49.00
Under-11s Seating: £10.00
Under-5s Seating: £5.00
Concessionary Seating: £15.00 – £39.00

FANS WITH DISABILITIES INFORMATION

Wheelchairs: 91 spaces for home fans and 9 spaces for visiting fans in special sections in the North Stand, Kop Stand and West Stand Lower. Ambulant fans with disabilities can sit in any section of the ground other than the Grandstand.
Helpers: Admitted
Prices: Normal prices for the disabled. Helpers free of charge
Disabled Toilets: Available in the North and West Stands
Commentaries are available for the blind
Contact: Dee Ashton (DLO) – 07142 212586 or e-mail: dee.ashton@swfc.co.uk   (Bookings are necessary)

Travelling Supporters' Information:
Routes: From the North, South and East: Exit the M1 at Junction 36 and follow signs to Sheffield (A61). Continue for 4 miles then take the 3rd exit at the 2nd roundabout into Leppings Lane. The ground is situated on the left; From the West: Take the A57 until the road splits in two. Take the left fork (A6101). After 3¾ miles turn left onto the one-way system and follow the road round to the right onto Holme Lane. This road becomes Bradfield Road. At the junction with the A61 (Penistone Road), turn left towards Barnsley. The stadium is on the left after Hillsborough Park.

SHREWSBURY TOWN FC

Founded: 1886 (**Entered League**: 1950)
Nickname: 'Salop' 'The Shrews' 'The Blues' 'Town'
Ground: Montgomery Waters Meadow, Oteley Road,
Shrewsbury   SY2 6ST
Ground Capacity: 9,875 (All seats)
Record Attendance: 18,917 (26th April 1961)
Pitch Size: 116 × 75 yards

Colours: Shirts and shorts are Blue and Amber
Telephone N°: (01743) 289177
Ticket Office: (01743) 273943
Fax Number: (01743) 246942
Web Site: www.shrewsburytown.com
E-mail: info@shrewsburytown.co.uk

GENERAL INFORMATION

Car Parking: Limited parking at the stadium – Permit
Holders only. Parking restrictions are imposed on matchdays
with no parking allowed in the vicinity of the stadium.
Visiting fans should use the Meole Brace Park & Ride Scheme
– £2.00 per person for the return journey – see details below
Coach Parking: At the stadium
Nearest Railway Station: Shrewsbury (2½ miles)
Nearest Bus Station: Raven Meadows, Shrewsbury
Club Shop: At the ground
Opening Times: Monday to Friday 9.00am to 5.00pm.
Saturday Matchdays 10.00am until kick-off.
Telephone N°: (01743) 289177

GROUND INFORMATION

Away Supporters' Entrances & Sections:
North Stand entrances and accommodation

ADMISSION INFO (2019/2020 PRICES)

Adult Seating: £20.00 – £22.00
Concessionary Seating: £15.00 – £17.00
Ages 12 to 18 Seating: £8.00 – £17.00
Ages 19 to 23/Student Seating: £15.00 – £17.00
Under-12s Seating: Free of charge
Note: Prices vary depending on the category of the game
Programme Price: £3.00

FANS WITH DISABILITIES INFORMATION

Wheelchairs: 94 spaces for home fans and 20 spaces for
away fans in the North, South and East Stands
Helpers: One helper admitted per fan with disabilities
Prices: Concessionary prices for fans with disabilities.
Helpers are admitted free of charge
Disabled Toilets: 30 available throughout the ground
Contact: (01743) 289177   (Bookings are necessary) –
lawrence.ellerby@shrewsburytown.co.uk (07970 440662)

Travelling Supporters' Information:
Park & Ride information: Buses run every 15 minutes from 12.30pm to 2.30pm on Saturday matchdays and 6.15pm to
7.30pm on matchdays in the week. Parking is free and the return bus journey is £2.00 per person. Buses return to the car parks
immediately after the match finishes and car parks will remain open for one hour only.   Car Park Locations:
Oxon Park and Ride Site: From the West and North West. At the junction of the A5 and the A458 (Churncote Roundabout)
follow the signs A458 'Shrewsbury Town Centre'. Oxon Park and Ride Site is clearly signposted;   **The Shirehall**: From all routes
proceed along the A5 to Emstrey Island Roundabout into Shrewsbury, take the A5064 along London Road to the Column
roundabout. Take the 3rd exit at the roundabout and the first right into the Shirehall Car Park; **Shirehall Overflow Car Park**:
Follow directions to London Road as above. Before you reach the roundabout the car park is on the right-hand side. Proceed on
foot to the Shirehall main car park for the bus.

SOUTHAMPTON FC

Founded: 1885 (**Entered League**: 1920)
Former Names: Southampton St. Mary's YMCA FC (1885-1897)
Nickname: 'Saints'
Ground: St. Mary's Stadium, Britannia Road, Southampton SO14 5FP
Ground Capacity: 32,384 (All seats)
Record Attendance: 32,363 (28th April 2012)

Pitch Size: 112 × 72 yards
Colours: Red and White shirts with Black shorts
Telephone N°: 02380 727700
Ticket Office: 02381 780780
General Fax Number: 02380 727727
Web Site: www.southamptonfc.com
E-mail: sfc@saintsfc.co.uk

GENERAL INFORMATION

Car Parking: Park & Ride must be pre-booked or Marina area car parks (£5.00)
Coach Parking: By Police direction
Nearest Railway Station: Southampton Central
Nearest Bus Station: Western Esplanade – services 7, 16, 18, X4 and X5 all travel to the stadium
Club Shop: At the ground and also at West Quay
Opening Times: Monday to Friday 9.00am to 5.00pm and Saturdays 9.30am to 5.00pm
Telephone N°: 02380 711973 (Stadium)
02380 337104 (West Quay)

GROUND INFORMATION

Away Supporters' Entrances & Sections:
Northam Stand – Blocks 43 to 48

ADMISSION INFO (2019/2020 PRICES)

Adult Seating: £20.00 – £65.00
Senior Citizen Seating: £20.00 – £65.00
Ages 18 to 25 Seating: £15.00 – £65.00
Under-18s Seating: £10.00 – £65.00
Under-11s Seating: £5.00 – £65.00
Note: Prices vary depending on the category of the game
Programme Price: £3.00

FANS WITH DISABILITIES INFORMATION

Wheelchairs: 193 spaces in total for Home and Away fans throughout the ground
Helpers: One helper admitted per fan with disabilities
Prices: Concessionary prices are charged
Disabled Toilets: Available in all Stands – Radar key required
Contact: 02380 711980 (Bookings are necessary)
E-mail Contact: supporterrelations@saintsfc.co.uk

Travelling Supporters' Information:
Routes: Although the ground is situated in the Melbourne Street/Marine Parade area of Southampton, no parking is available in the immediate vicinity except by special arrangement for Disabled supporters. There are a number of well-signposted Park and Ride car parks around the City and those designated for Away fans should be clearly marked.

SOUTHEND UNITED FC

Founded: 1906 (**Entered League**: 1920)
Former Name: Southend Athletic FC
Nickname: 'Shrimpers' 'Blues'
Ground: Roots Hall Ground, Victoria Avenue,
Southend-on-Sea   SS2 6NQ
Ground Capacity: 12,392 (All seats)
Record Attendance: 31,033 (10th January 1979)

Pitch Size: 110 × 74 yards
Colours: Blue shirts and shorts
Telephone N°: (01702) 304050
Ticket Office: 08444 770077
Web Site: www.southendunited.co.uk
E-mail: info@southend-united.co.uk

GENERAL INFORMATION

Car Parking: Available at Southend High School for Boys
(Post code SS0 0RG). £5.00 fee and a 10 minute walk
Coach Parking: Car park at the ground. Coach drivers
should contact the club prior to the game
Nearest Railway Station: Prittlewell (¼ mile)
Nearest Bus Station: London Road, Southend
Club Shop: At the ground
Opening Times: Monday to Friday 9.30am to 5.00pm and
Saturday Matchdays 10.00am to 3.00pm
Telephone N°: (01702) 351117

GROUND INFORMATION

Away Supporters' Entrances & Sections:
Turnstiles 13 to 16 for North Stand seating

ADMISSION INFO (2020/2021 PRICES)

Adult Seating: £25.00
Concessionary Seating: £18.00
Under-23s/Student Seating: £17.00
Under-17s Seating: £12.00
Under-9s Seating: £5.00
Note: Tickets are cheaper when purchased in advance.
Programme Price: £3.00

FANS WITH DISABILITIES INFORMATION

Wheelchairs: 20 spaces for Home fans and and 6 spaces for
Away fans in a special section in the West Stand
Helpers: One helper admitted per fan with disabilities
Prices: Concessionary prices apply for fans with disabilities.
Helpers receive complimentary tickets
Disabled Toilets: Available – Radar key required
Commentaries are available for the blind
Contact: (01702) 304050 (Gavin Preston)
or e-mail ticket.officemanager@southend-united.co.uk

Travelling Supporters' Information:
Routes: From the North and West: From the M25 take Junction 29 and follow the A127 to Southend. About 1 mile outside of
Southend Town Centre, take the 3rd exit at the roundabout into Victoria Avenue for the ground; From the A13: Follow signs for
Southend, turn left into West Road at Westcliff. At the end of West Road turn left into Victoria Avenue – the ground is on the left.

STEVENAGE FC

Founded: 1976
Former Names: None
Nickname: 'Boro'
Ground: Lamex Stadium, Broadhall Way, Stevenage, Hertfordshire   SG2 8RH
Record Attendance: 8,040   (25th January 1998)
Pitch Size: 110 × 70 yards

Colours: Red and White shirts with Red shorts
Telephone Nº: (01438) 223223
Ground Capacity: 7,800
Seating Capacity: 3,404
Web site: www.stevenagefc.com
E-mail: info@stevenagefc.com

GENERAL INFORMATION

Car Parking: Fairlands Show Ground (opposite)
Coach Parking: None at the Stadium
Nearest Railway Station: Stevenage (1 mile)
Nearest Bus Station: Stevenage
Club Shop: At the ground
Opening Times: Tuesday and Friday 10.00am to 5.00pm, Thursday 10.00am to 7.00pm, Tuesday and Saturday Matchdays from 12.00pm to kick-off then for 15 minutes after the game.
Telephone Nº: (01438) 223223

GROUND INFORMATION

Away Supporters' Entrances & Sections:
South Stand entrances and accommodation

ADMISSION INFO (2019/2020 PRICES)

Adult Standing: £20.00
Adult Seating: £24.00
Under-18s Standing: £12.00
Under-18s Seating: £16.00
Under-12s Standing: £5.00
Under-12s Seating: £10.00
Concessionary Standing: £17.00
Concessionary Seating: £22.00
Programme Price: £3.00

FANS WITH DISABILITIES INFORMATION

Wheelchairs: 13 spaces available by the North Terrace
Helpers: Admitted
Prices: Concessionary prices apply for fans with disabilities. Free of charge for helpers
Disabled Toilets: Yes
Contact: (01438) 218072   (Bookings are necessary)
Lindsay Powell –   lindsayp@stevenagefc.com

Travelling Supporters' Information:
Routes: Exit the A1(M) at Junction 7 and take the B197. The ground is on the right at the 2nd roundabout.
Bus Routes: SB4 and SB5

STOKE CITY FC

Founded: 1863 (**Entered League**: 1888)
Former Name: Stoke FC
Nickname: 'The Potters'
Ground: bet365 Stadium, Stanley Matthews Way, Stoke-on-Trent ST4 4EG
Ground Capacity: 30,089 (All seats)
Record Attendance: 30,022 (17th March 2018)

Pitch Size: 115 × 74 yards
Colours: Red and White striped shirts, White shorts
Telephone Nº: (01782) 367598 or (01782) 592233
Ticket Office: (01782) 367599
Fax Number: (01782) 592201
Web Site: www.stokecityfc.com
E-mail: info@stokecityfc.com

GENERAL INFORMATION

Car Parking: At the ground (bookings necessary). Also various car parks within 10 minutes walk
Coach Parking: At the ground
Nearest Railway Station: Stoke-on-Trent (1½ miles)
Nearest Bus Station: Glebe Street, Stoke-on-Trent
Club Shop: At the ground and at the Potteries Shopping Centre in Hanley
Opening Times: Weekdays 9.00am–5.30pm, non-match Saturdays 9.00am–2.00pm. Weekend Matchdays 9.00am to kick-off then 30 minutes after the final whistle. Evening games 9.00am to kick-off and 30 minutes after the game. Potteries Store: Monday to Saturday 9.00am–6.00pm (until 8.00pm on Thursday) and Sunday 10.30am to 4.30pm.
Telephone Nº: (01782) 592242 (shop at the ground) and (01782) 592132 (Potteries shop)

GROUND INFORMATION

Away Supporters' Sections: South Stand

ADMISSION INFO (2018/2019 PRICES)

Adult Seating: £25.00 – £50.00
Under-17s Seating: £15.00 – £27.00
Under-11s Seating: £8.00 – £24.00
Senior Citizen Seating: £19.00 – £35.00
Note: Prices vary depending on the category of the game
Programme Price: £3.50

FANS WITH DISABILITIES INFORMATION

Wheelchairs: 186 spaces available for home fans and 26 spaces available for away fans
Helpers: One helper admitted per disabled person
Prices: Concessionary prices for disabled fan. Helpers free
Disabled Toilets: Available
Commentaries are available – phone for details
Contact: (01782) 367598   (Bookings are necessary) or e-mail accessibility@stokecityfc.com

Travelling Supporters' Information:
Routes: From the North, South and West: Exit the M6 at Junction 15 and take the A500 to Stoke-on-Trent then the A50 towards Derby/Uttoxeter (the bet365 Stadium is signposted and visible to the right). Once on the A50 take the fist exit, turn right at the traffic lights and cross over the flyover. Turn right at the first roundabout, left at the next roundabout and right at the third roundabout for the stadium; From the East: Take the A50 to Stoke-on-Trent and take the last turn-off (signposted for bet365 Stadium). Go straight on at the first roundabout then right at the second roundabout to reach the stadium.

SUNDERLAND AFC

Founded: 1879 (**Entered League**: 1890)
Former Names: Sunderland and District Teachers FC
Nickname: 'The Black Cats'
Ground: Stadium of Light, Sunderland   SR5 1SU
Ground Capacity: 48,707 (All seats)
Record Attendance: 48,353 (13th April 2002)
Pitch Size: 110 × 74 yards (101 × 68 metres)

Colours: Red and White striped shirts, Black shorts
Telephone Nº: 0371 911-1200
Ticket Office: 0371 911-1973
Fax Number: (0191) 551-5123
Web Site: www.safc.com
E-mail: enquiries@safc.com

GENERAL INFORMATION

Car Parking: Park and Ride from Wessington Way (SR5 3XG)
Coach Parking: At the ground – must be pre-booked
Nearest Railway Station: Sunderland (1 mile)
Nearest Bus Station: Town Centre (1 mile)
Club Shop: At the Stadium, plus smaller stores at Debenhams in Sunderland
Opening Times: Monday to Saturday 9.00am – 5.30pm and Sunday 10.00am to 4.00pm
Telephone Nº: (0191) 551-5375

GROUND INFORMATION

Away Supporters' Entrances & Sections:
Carling North Stand (Upper Tier)

ADMISSION INFO (2018/2019 PRICES)

Adult Seating: £18.00 – £45.00
Senior Citizen Seating: £15.00 – £45.00
Under-22s Seating: £10.00 – £45.00
Under-16s Seating: £7.50 – £45.00
Note: Prices for the 2020/2021 season were not available at the time of going to press. Please contact the club for details.
Programme Price: £3.00

FANS WITH DISABILITIES INFORMATION

Wheelchairs: 202 spaces in total throughout the stadium
Helpers: Admitted
Prices: Normal prices for fans with disabilities. Helpers free
Disabled Toilets: Available in all stands and Corporate areas
Contact: 0371 911-1200   (Bookings are necessary) – chris.waters@safc.com (Disability Liaison Officer)

Travelling Supporters' Information:
Routes: From All Parts: Exit the A1 at the A690 Durham/Sunderland exit. After approximately 4 miles turn left onto the A19 (signposted Tyne Tunnel). Keep in the left lane and take the slip road (signposted Washington/Sunderland) onto the bridge over the River Wear. Turn right onto the A1231 (signposted Washington/Sunderland), stay on this road going straight across 4 roundabouts into Sunderland. Continue straight through 2 sets of traffic lights and the Stadium car park is on the right, about 1 mile past the traffic lights.

SWANSEA CITY FC

Founded: 1912 (**Entered League**: 1920)	**Pitch Size**: 115 × 74 yards
Former Name: Swansea Town FC (1912-1970)	**Colours**: White and Black shirts, shorts and socks
Nickname: 'The Swans'	**Telephone Nº**: (01792) 616400
Ground: Liberty Stadium, Landore, Swansea, SA1 2FA	**Ticket Office**: (01792) 616400 Option 1
Ground Capacity: 21,000 (All seats)	**Fax Number**: (01792) 616606
Record Attendance: 32,796 (at the Vetch Field)	**Web Site**: www.swanseacity.com
	E-mail: info@swanseacityfc.co.uk

GENERAL INFORMATION

Car Parking: Reserved parking only at the stadium but 3,000 spaces are available in a Park & Ride scheme just off Junction 45 of the M4.

Coach Parking: By Police direction

Nearest Railway Station: Swansea High Street (1½ miles)

Nearest Bus Station: Quadrant Depot (2½ miles)

Club Shop: At the ground

Opening Times: Monday to Friday 10.00am to 5.00pm, Saturday from 9.00am to 5.00pm and Sunday 10.00am to 4.00pm

Telephone Nº: (01792) 616546

GROUND INFORMATION

Away Supporters' Entrances & Sections:
North Stand

ADMISSION INFO (2019/2020 PRICES)

Adult Seating: £25.00 – £30.00

Concessionary Seating: £15.00 – £17.50

Under-18s Seating: £10.00 – £15.00

Under-12s Seating: £5.00

Note: A £2.50 ticket booking fee applies (£1.25 online). Discounted prices are available for members.

Programme Price: £3.00

FANS WITH DISABILITIES INFORMATION

Wheelchairs: 135 spaces available for home fans and helpers and 15 spaces available for away fans and helpers

Helpers: One helper admitted per wheelchair

Prices: Normal prices apply for fans with disabilities. Free of charge for helpers

Disabled Toilets: Available

There are a number of disabled parking spaces available at the stadium

Contact: (01792) 616611 (Bookings are necessary)
Mark Phillips – markphillips@swanseacity.com

Travelling Supporters' Information:
Routes: From All Parts: Exit the M4 at Junction 45 and follow signs for Swansea (A4067). The stadium is clearly signposted.

SWINDON TOWN FC

Founded: 1881 (**Entered League**: 1920)
Nickname: 'Robins'
Ground: The Energy Check County Ground, County Road, Swindon SN1 2ED
Ground Capacity: 15,547 (All seats)
Record Attendance: 32,000 (15th January 1972)
Pitch Size: 110 × 70 yards

Colours: Red shirts and shorts
Telephone Nº: 0330 002-1879
Ticket Office: 0330 002-1879
Web Site: www.swindontownfc.co.uk
E-mail: reception@swindontownfc.co.uk

GENERAL INFORMATION

Car Parking: Town Centre, street Parking and local matchday car parks
Coach Parking: Car park adjacent to the ground
Nearest Railway Station: Swindon (½ mile)
Nearest Bus Station: Swindon (½ mile)
Club Shop: The Swindon Town Superstore
Opening Times: Weekdays 9.00am – 5.00pm, Non-Matchday Saturdays 9.00am – 12.00pm and Saturday Matchdays 9.00am to 6.00pm
Telephone Nº: 0330 002-1879

GROUND INFORMATION

Away Supporters' Entrances & Sections:
Arkell's Stand turnstiles for the Stratton Bank

ADMISSION INFO (2019/2020 PRICES)

Adult Seating: £19.00 – £23.00
Concessionary Seating: £15.00 – £17.00
Under-21s Seating: £10.00
Under-18s Seating: £6.00
Under-11s Seating: £2.00
Note: A selection of family tickets are also available
Programme Price: £3.00

FANS WITH DISABILITIES INFORMATION

Wheelchairs: 56 spaces in total for Home and Away fans in a special section in front of Arkell's Stand (50 home, 6 away)
Helpers: One helper admitted with each fan in a wheelchair
Prices: Concessionary prices for fans with disabilities. Helpers are admitted free of charge.
Disabled Toilets: Available
Commentaries are available for the blind
Contact: 0330 002-1879 (Bookings are necessary) – markisaacs@swindontownafc.co.uk (DLO) – 07525 017305

Travelling Supporters' Information:
Routes: From London, the East and the South: Exit the M4 at Junction 15 and take the A345 into Swindon along Queen's Drive. Take the 3rd exit at 'Magic Roundabout' into County Road; From the West: Exit the M4 at Junction 15 then as above; From the North: Take the M4 or A345/A420/A361 to the County Road roundabout, then as above.

TOTTENHAM HOTSPUR FC

Founded: 1882 (**Entered League**: 1908)
Former Name: Hotspur FC (1882-1884)
Nickname: 'Spurs'
Ground: Tottenham Hotspur Stadium, White Hart Lane, Bill Nicholson Way, 782 High Road, Tottenham, London N17 0BX
Ground Capacity: 62,062 (All seats)

Record Attendance: 61,104 (vs Chelsea, 22/12/19)
Colours: White shirts with Navy Blue shorts
Telephone Nº: 0344 499-5000
Ticket Office: 0344 844-0102
Fax Number: 01992 844102
Web Site: www.tottenhamhotspur.com
E-mail: supporter.services@tottenhamhotspur.com

GENERAL INFORMATION

Car Parking: None within ¼ mile of the ground
Coach Parking: Northumberland Park, West Road – Parking permit required
Nearest Railway Station: White Hart Lane (nearby) or Northumberland Park
Nearest Tube Station: Seven Sisters (Victoria Line) or Manor House (Piccadilly Line)
Club Shop: At the stadium and in Chelmsford, Harlow and Stevenage
Opening Times: Stadium store: Monday to Saturday 9.30am – 5.30pm and Sunday 10.00am – 4.00pm. The stores in Chelmsford, Harlow and Stevenage close at 4.30pm from Monday to Saturday.
Telephone Nº: 0344 499-5000 or (020) 8365-5042

GROUND INFORMATION

Away Supporters' Entrances & Sections:
North east corner of the stadium – Blocks 114-118 & 234

ADMISSION INFO (2019/2020 PRICES)

Adult Seating: £30.00 – £98.00
Senior Citizen Seating: £15.00 – £35.00
Under-22s Seating: £22.50 – £52.50
Under-18s Seating: £15.00 – £35.00

FANS WITH DISABILITIES INFORMATION

Wheelchairs: 265 spaces available in total around the stadium. Away fans in wheelchairs please use entrance 11a.
Helpers: Admitted
Prices: Normal prices for disabled fans. Helpers free of charge
Disabled Toilets: 66 available throughout the stadium
Contact: (020) 8365-5360 (Bookings are necessary)
Oliver Riley (DAO) – oliver.riley@tottenhamhotspur.com

Travelling Supporters' Information:
Routes: From All Parts: Take the A406 North Circular to Edmonton and at traffic lights follow signs for Tottenham (A1010) into Fore Street for the ground.

TRANMERE ROVERS FC

Founded: 1884
Former Name: Belmont FC
Nickname: 'Rovers' 'Super White Army'
Ground: Prenton Park, Prenton Road West,
Birkenhead CH42 9PY
Ground Capacity: 16,567 (All seats)
Record Attendance: 24,424 (5th February 1972)

Pitch Size: 110 × 70 yards
Colours: White shirts with Blue shorts
Telephone Nº: 03330 144452
Ticket Office: 03330 144452 Option 2
Fax Number: (0151) 609-0606
Web Site: www.tranmererovers.co.uk
E-mail: customerservice@tranmererovers.co.uk

GENERAL INFORMATION

Car Parking: Large car park at the ground (£5.00 per car)
Coach Parking: At the ground (£10.00 charge)
Nearest Railway Stations: Hamilton Square, Rock Ferry and Conway Park (approximately 1½ miles)
Nearest Bus Station: Conway Park (Town Centre)
Club Shop: At the ground
Opening Times: Thursday to Saturday 9.00am to 5.00pm
Telephone Nº: 03330 144452 Option 1

GROUND INFORMATION

Away Supporters' Entrances & Sections:
Cowshed Stand turnstiles 5-9 – access from Borough Road
(Away section capacity: 2,500)

ADMISSION INFO (2020/2021 PRICES)

Adult Seating: £22.00 – £25.00
Under-12s Seating: £2.00 – £5.00
Under-18s Seating: £9.00 – £10.00
Senior Citizen Seating: £15.00 – £18.00
Young Persons Ticket (Ages 18-22): £15.00 – £18.00
Programme Price: £3.00
Note: Discounted prices are available for advance purchases. Under-12s must be accompanied by an adult.

FANS WITH DISABILITIES INFORMATION

Wheelchairs: 54 spaces in total for Home and Away fans in the disabled section, Bebington Paddock
Helpers: One helper admitted per fan with disabilities
Prices: £15.00 – £18.00 for fans with disabilities (with a free ticket for a carer)
Disabled Toilets: 2 available in the disabled section
Contact: (0151) 609-3380 (Bookings are necessary) – christiner@tranmererovers.co.uk (Disability Liaison Officer)

Travelling Supporters' Information:
Routes: From the North: From Liverpool city centre, travel through the Kingsway (Wallasey) Mersey Tunnel (£1.70 toll for cars) then continue onto the M53, exiting at Junction 3. Take the first exit (signposted Birkenhead), continue past Sainsbury's then turn right at the traffic lights by the Halfway House pub then turn left into Prenton Road West at the next set of lights. The ground is on the right after a short distance. From the South: Exit the M53 at Junction 4 and take the 4th exit at the roundabout onto the B5151 Mount Road (the ground is signposted from here). After 2½ miles, turn right at the traffic lights (by the United Reformed Church) into Prenton Road West for the ground.

WALSALL FC

Founded: 1888 (**Entered League**: 1892)
Former Name: Walsall Town Swifts FC (1888-1895)
Nickname: 'Saddlers'
Ground: Banks's Stadium, Bescot Crescent, Walsall,
West Midlands   WS1 4SA
Ground Capacity: 11,300 (All seats)
Record Attendance: 11,049 (9th May 2004)
Pitch Size: 110 × 73 yards

Colours: Red shirts with White shorts
Telephone Nº: (01922) 622791
Ticket Office: (01922) 651416 or (01922) 651414
Fax Number: (01922) 613202
Web Site: www.saddlers.co.uk
E-mail: info@walsallfc.co.uk

GENERAL INFORMATION

Car Parking: Car park at the ground
Coach Parking: At the ground
Nearest Railway Station: Bescot (adjacent)
Nearest Bus Station: Bradford Place, Walsall
Club Shop: At the ground
Opening Times: Weekdays 9.00am – 4.30pm and Saturday
Matchdays 10.00am to 5.30pm
Telephone Nº: (01922) 651410

GROUND INFORMATION

Away Supporters' Entrances & Sections:
Turnstiles 21-28 for the University of Wolverhampton Stand

ADMISSION INFO (2019/2020 PRICES)

Adult Seating: £20.00 – £22.00
Child Seating: £11.00 – £13.00
Concessionary Seating: £16.00 – £18.00
Note: Discounts are available for advance bookings and
savings from Family Tickets are available in some stands
Programme Price: £3.00

FANS WITH DISABILITIES INFORMATION

Wheelchairs: 33 spaces in total for Home and Away fans in
the a special section in the St. Francis Group Community Stand
Helpers: One helper admitted with each fan with disabilities
Prices: Normal prices apply for fans with disabilities.
Helpers are admitted free of charge
Disabled Toilets: 5 available around the ground
A special Lounge for fans with disabilities is available
Contact: (01922) 651416   (Bookings are necessary)
Laura Greenhouse (DLO) – laura.greenhouse@walsall.co.uk

Travelling Supporters' Information:
Routes: From All Parts: Exit the M6 at Junction 9 turning North towards Walsall onto the A461. After ¼ mile turn right into
Wallows Lane and pass over the railway bridge. Then take the 1st right into Bescot Crescent and the ground is ½ mile along on
the left adjacent to Bescot Railway Station.

WATFORD FC

Founded: 1881 (**Entered League**: 1920)
Former Names: Formed by the amalgamation of West Herts FC and St. Mary's FC
Nickname: 'Hornets'
Ground: Vicarage Road Stadium, Watford, WD18 0ER
Ground Capacity: 21,577 (All seats)
Record Attendance: 34,099 (3rd February 1969)

Pitch Size: 114 × 73 yards
Colours: Yellow & Black striped shirts, Black shorts
Telephone N°: (01923) 496000
Ticket Office: (01923) 223023
Fax Number: (01923) 496001
Web Site: www.watfordfc.com
E-mail: yourvoice@watfordfc.com

GENERAL INFORMATION

Car Parking: Nearby multi-storey car parks and schools
Coach Parking: By Police direction
Nearest Railway Station: Watford Junction or Watford Tube Station (Metropolitan Line)
Nearest Bus Station: Watford Town Centre
Club Shop: The Hornets Shop at Vicarage Road Stadium and at Intu Watford
Opening Times: Monday to Saturday 9.00am to 6.00pm at the stadium. Intu Watford: Monday to Wednesday 9.00am to 6.00pm , Thursday to Saturday 9.00am to 8.00pm and Sunday 11.00am to 5.00pm
Telephone N°: (01923) 496000

GROUND INFORMATION

Away Supporters' Entrances & Sections:
Vicarage Road End entrances and accommodation

ADMISSION INFO (2019/2020 PRICES)

Adult Seating: £30.00 – £42.00
Under-16s Seating: £5.00 – £20.00
Student Seating: £18.00 – £24.00
Senior Citizen Seating: £22.00 – £28.00
Programme Price: £3.50

FANS WITH DISABILITIES INFORMATION

Wheelchairs: 151 spaces in total in accessible platforms located in all 4 stands.
Prices and Helpers: Normal prices for fans with disabilities. One assistant is admitted free with each fan with disabilities
Disabled Toilets: Available
Commentaries available around the ground – no charge
Contact: (01923) 223023 (Bookings in advance helpful)
Shelley Newman (DLO) – shelley.newman@watfordfc.com

Travelling Supporters' Information:
Routes: Vicarage Road is closed to traffic from 2 hours before kick-off on matchday. The following directions lead to the nearest car park: From the North and East: Exit the M25 at Junction 20 and take the first exit onto the A41. At the next roundabout, take the second exit onto A411 (Hempstead Road).* Continue along the A411 to the town centre. At the large roundabout take the second exit feeding into the inner ring road, which is a one-way system. Stay in the righthand lane and follow the Ring Road until you see the entrance to the Church car park on your right hand side; From the South and West: Exit the M25 at Junction 19 then take the third exit at the roundabout onto A411 (Hempstead Road). Then as from * above; From Central London: Exit the M1 Junction 5 and take the second exit onto the A4008. Cross the first roundabout, then take the second exit at the next towards the town centre. At the traffic lights, turn left onto the inner ring road at the T-junction and filter across to the right-hand lane. Follow the Ring Road until you see the entrance to the Church car park on your right hand side.

WEST BROMWICH ALBION FC

Founded: 1879 (**Entered League**: 1888)
Former Name: West Bromwich Strollers (1879-1880)
Nickname: 'Throstles' 'Baggies' 'Albion'
Ground: The Hawthorns, Halfords Lane,
West Bromwich, West Midlands   B71 4LF
Ground Capacity: 26,850 (All seats)
Record Attendance: 64,815 (6th March 1937)

Pitch Size: 115 × 74 yards
Colours: Navy Blue & White striped shirts, White shorts
Telephone N°: 0871 271-1100
Ticket Office: (0121) 227-2227
Fax Number: 0871 271-9821
Web Site: www.wba.co.uk
E-mail: enquiries@wbafc.co.uk

GENERAL INFORMATION

Car Parking: Halfords Lane Car Parks, East Stand Car Park and several independent car parks
Coach Parking: At the ground
Nearest Railway Station: Hawthorns (200 yards) or Rolfe Street, Smethwick (1½ miles)
Nearest Midland Metro: Hawthorns (200 yards)
Nearest Bus Station: West Bromwich Town Centre
Club Shop: At the ground and at the Merry Hill Centre
Opening Times: Weekdays 9.00am – 5.00pm, Saturday Matchdays 9.00am – 2.45pm and Sundays 10.00am – 2.00pm Merryhill Centre: Monday to Saturday 10.00am to 4.00pm and Sunday 11.00am to 5.00pm
Telephone N°: 0871 271-9790 (Stadium Megastore), 0871 271-9793 (Merry Hill Centre)

GROUND INFORMATION

Away Supporters' Entrances & Sections:
Smethwick End 'A' turnstiles

ADMISSION INFO (2019/2020 PRICES)

Adult Seating: £20.00 – £23.00
Concessionary Seating: £15.00 – £17.00
Under-23s/Student Seating: £15.00
Under-18s Seating: £10.00
Under-11s Seating: £5.00
Programme Price: £3.00

FANS WITH DISABILITIES INFORMATION

Wheelchairs: 171 spaces in total in special sections in the Birmingham Road End, Smethwick End and East Stand
Helpers: One helper admitted with each fan with disabilities (subject to availability of space)
Prices: £10.00 – £15.00 for fans with disabilities. Helpers free
Disabled Toilets: 14 in total available around the ground
Contact: (0121) 227-2227   (Bookings are necessary) – Liz Massey (DLO) – liz.massey@wbafc.co.uk

Travelling Supporters' Information:
Routes: From All Parts: Exit the M5 at Junction 1 and follow Matchday signs for the ground. The matchday traffic plan has made the "obvious" route via the A41 unusable for home games.

WEST HAM UNITED FC

Photograph courtesy of Queen Elizabeth Olympic Park

Founded: 1895 (**Entered League**: 1919)
Former Name: Thames Ironworks FC
Nickname: 'Hammers'
Ground: London Stadium, Queen Elizabeth Olympic Park, Marsh Gate Lane, London   E20 2ST
Ground Capacity: 60,000 (All seats)
Record Attendance: 59,988 (vs Everton 30/3/2019)

Pitch Size: 115 × 74 yards
Colours: Claret and Blue shirts with White shorts
Telephone Nº: (020) 8548-2748
Ticket Office: 03330 301966
Web Site: www.whufc.com
E-mail: supporterservices@westhamunited.co.uk

GENERAL INFORMATION

Car Parking: Limited spaces available at the Olympic Park. See Travelling Supporters' Information below for more details
Nearest Railway Station: Stratford (20 minutes walk)
Nearest Tube Station: Stratford (20 minutes walk)
Club Shops: At the Stadium and also at Lakeside Thurrock, Liberty Romford and Basildon
Opening Times: Vary by store. Stadium opening hours are Monday to Saturday 9.30am to 5.00pm (from 9.00am on Saturdays) and Sunday 11.00am to 5.00pm.
Telephone Nº: (01708) 890258 (Lakeside Store) or (01708) 741877 (Liberty Romford)

GROUND INFORMATION

Away Supporters' Entrances & Sections:
South West corner of the stadium – Block D

ADMISSION INFO (2019/2020 PRICES)

Adult Seating: £30.00 – £80.00
Senior Citizen Seating: £18.00 – £80.00
Under-21s Seating: £18.00 – £80.00
Under-16s Seating: £18.00 – £80.00
Programme Price: £3.50

FANS WITH DISABILITIES INFORMATION

Wheelchairs: 253 spaces available throughout the stadium inncluding 24 for away fans
Helpers: Admitted
Prices: Concessionary prices apply for fans with disabilities. Free of charge for helpers
Disabled Toilets: 49 available in all areas of the stadium
Contact: 03330 300174   (Bookings are necessary) or accessibility@westhamunited.co.uk (Julie Pidgeon)

Travelling Supporters' Information:
Routes: Due to the fact that there is restricted car parking in the area of the stadium, it is recommended that visitors use the many public transport links available nearby, with tube and rail links plus numerous bus and coach routes close to the stadium. For those who choose to travel by car, the stadium is located in the Stratford area of east London, just to the east of the A12 and to the north of the River Thames. Visitors travelling by car are advised to use the public car parks at the Westfield Stratford City shopping centre, Stratford International station and the Stratford Centre.

WIGAN ATHLETIC FC

Founded: 1932 (**Entered League**: 1978)
Nickname: 'Latics'
Ground: DW Stadium, Loire Drive, Wigan, Lancashire WN5 0UZ
Ground Capacity: 25,146 (All seats)
Record Attendance: 25,133 (11th May 2008)
Pitch Size: 115 × 74 yards

Colours: Blue and White striped shirts, Blue shorts
Telephone Nº: (01942) 774000
Ticket Office: (01942) 311111
Web Site: www.wiganathletic.com
E-mail: feedback@wiganathletic.com

GENERAL INFORMATION

Car Parking: 2,000 spaces available at the ground (£5.00 for cars, £10.00 for minibuses, £20.00 for coaches)
Coach Parking: At the ground
Nearest Railway Station: Wallgate and Wigan North Western (1 mile)
Nearest Bus Station: Wigan
Club Shop: At the Stadium
Opening Times: Monday to Friday 10.00am to 5.00pm, Non-match Saturdays 10.00am to 4.00pm, Saturday Matchdays 10.00am to kick-off plus 30 minutes after the game
Telephone Nº: (01942) 770450

GROUND INFORMATION

Away Supporters' Entrances & Sections: North Stand

ADMISSION INFO (2019/2020 PRICES)

Adult Seating: £20.00 – £30.00
Senior Citizen Seating: £15.00
Under-18s Seating: £10.00
Under-12s Seating: £5.00
Under-5s Seating: £2.00
Programme Price: £3.00

FANS WITH DISABILITIES INFORMATION

Wheelchairs: 206 spaces available in total
Helpers: One helper admitted with each fan with disabilities
Prices: Normal prices for fans with disabilities. Helpers free
Disabled Toilets: 20 available in total
Contact: (01942) 774000   (Bookings are necessary) – Louise Peet (DLO) – l.peet@dwstadium.com

Travelling Supporters' Information:
Routes: From North: Exit M6 at Junction 27, turn left at end of slip road then right at T-junction, signposted Shevington. After 1 mile turn left at the mini-roundabout into Old Lane (B5375). After approx. 2 miles winding through countryside turn right at traffic lights into Scot Lane. Stadium is next left; From South & West: Exit M6 at Junction 25 follow signs for Wigan (A49). After approx. 2 miles a complex junction is reached, keep in left-hand lane (McDonalds on right). Turn left at traffic light filter lane into Robin Park Road. Turn right at third set of traffic lights and follow road to stadium; From East: Exit M61 Junction 6, take 1st exit at roundabout. At next roundabout take 1st left into Chorley Road. Follow signs for Wigan B5238, first turning right then left at Aspull Roundabout. After 2 miles turn right at traffic lights after Earl of Balcarres Pub to face Tesco. Turn left at lights, keep in left lane turn left at next lights with the Quality Hotel on the corner. Follow ring road, get into second lane from right as road bears right into Caroline Street, signposted Orrell. Continue on ring road as it bears left passing B&Q on left, pass Wigan Pier on right and as road goes under railway bridge get into right hand lane to turn right at lights into Robin Park Road. Then South & West.

WOLVERHAMPTON WANDERERS FC

Founded: 1877 (**Entered League**: 1888)
Former Names: Formed by the amalgamation of St. Luke's FC and The Wanderers Football & Cricket Club in 1879. St. Luke's is considered the start of the club
Nickname: 'Wolves'
Ground: Molineux Stadium, Waterloo Road, Wolverhampton   WV1 4QR
Ground Capacity: 31,700 (All seats)

Record Attendance: 61,305 (11th February 1939)
Pitch Size: 110 × 75 yards
Colours: Gold shirts with Black shorts
Telephone Nº: 0371 222-2220
Ticket Office: 0371 222-1877
Fax Number: (01902) 687006
Web Site: www.wolves.co.uk
E-mail: help@wolves.co.uk

GENERAL INFORMATION

Car Parking: Around West Park, Newhampton Road and rear of the Stan Cullis Stand. Also in City Centre (5 minutes walk)
Coach Parking: By Police direction
Nearest Railway Station: Wolverhampton (¾ mile)
Nearest Bus Station: Wolverhampton (¾ mile)
Club Shop: At the ground
Opening Times: Daily from 9.00am to 5.00pm
Telephone Nº: 0371 222-2220 Option 1

GROUND INFORMATION

Away Supporters' Entrances & Sections:
Steve Bull Stand Lower Tier (turnstiles for Block 3)

ADMISSION INFO (2019/2020 PRICES)

Adult Seating: £25.00 – £46.00
Senior Citizen/Under-21s Seating: £15.00 – £26.50
Under-17s Seating: £11.50 – £18.50
Under-12s Seating: £6.00 – £15.00
Programme Price: £3.00

FANS WITH DISABILITIES INFORMATION

Wheelchairs: 115 spaces for home fans in the Stan Cullis Stand and Billy Wright Family Enclosure plus 14 spaces for away fans in the Steve Bull Lower Stand
Helpers: Admitted
Prices: Please contact the club for details
Disabled Toilets: At both ends of the Stan Cullis Stand
Contact: (01902) 828312   Laura Wright (DAO) – laurawright@wolves.co.uk

Travelling Supporters' Information:
Routes: From North: Exit M6 Junction 12. At island take 3rd exit onto A5 for Wolverhampton. At next island turn left onto A449. After 6 miles A449 passes under M54, carry straight on and at 6th roundabout (Five Ways) take 3rd exit into Waterloo Road. Molineux is 1 mile straight on; From South West: Exit M5 Junction 2, follow signs for Wolverhampton on A4123 for 8 miles to ring road. Turn left on ring road (follow Molineux Centre signs). Take 2nd exit at next 2 islands * Pass Bank's Brewery and Swimming Baths on left and turn left at next set of traffic lights. Molineux is 500 yards on right; From South/East: Exit M6 Junction 10, take A454 (via Willenhall) to Wolverhampton ring road. At first ring road island take 4th exit (A449 to Stafford). Straight on at next 2 sets of traffic lights. Filter right at third set of lights (Waterloo Road). Molineux is 500 yards on right; From West: Take A41 to Wolverhampton ring road roundabout. Turn left into the ring road. Then as from the South West *

WYCOMBE WANDERERS FC

Founded: 1887 (**Entered League**: 1993)
Nickname: 'The Blues' 'The Chairboys'
Ground: Adams Park, Hillbottom Road, Sands,
High Wycombe   HP12 4HJ
Ground Capacity: 9,448
Seating Capacity: 8,250
Record Attendance: 10,000 (vs Chelsea, July 2005)

Pitch Size: 115 × 75 yards
Colours: Navy and Light Blue quarters with Navy shorts
Telephone Nº: (01494) 472100
Ticket Office: (01494) 441118
Fax Number: (01494) 441589
Web Site: www.wycombewanderers.co.uk
E-mail: wwfc@wwfc.com

GENERAL INFORMATION

Car Parking: Car park at the ground (£5.00) and also in Hillbottom Road
Coach Parking: Car park at the ground
Nearest Railway Station: High Wycombe
Nearest Bus Station: High Wycombe
Club Shop: At the ground
Opening Times: Monday to Friday 10.00am to 5.00pm but closed on Wednesdays. Also open from 10.00am on Saturday matchdays
Telephone Nº: (01494) 509510

GROUND INFORMATION

Away Supporters' Entrances & Sections:
Lords Builders Merchants Stand (seating only)

ADMISSION INFO (2020/2021 PRICES)

Adult Standing: £18.00   **Adult Seating**: £20.00–£26.00
Ages 22-25 Standing: £14.00   **Seating**: £16.00–£21.00
Ages 19-21 Standing: £13.00   **Seating**: £14.00–£20.00
Ages 12-18 Standing: £8.00   **Seating**: £5.00–£15.00
Senior Citizen Standing: £15.00   **Seating**: £17–£23
Under-12s Standing/Seating: £1.00 – £10.00
Note: A £2.00 discount is available for advance purchases
Programme Price: £3.50

FANS WITH DISABILITIES INFORMATION

Wheelchairs: 32 spaces in total available in special sections of the Family Stand and Away Stand
Helpers: One helper admitted per wheelchair
Prices: Full price for fans with disabilities. Free for helpers
Disabled Toilets: 4 available in the Family Stand
Commentaries are available for 5 people
Contact: (01494) 441118   (Bookings are not necessary) or e-mail tickets@wwfc.com (Lily Fulker)

Travelling Supporters' Information:
Routes: From All Parts: Exit the M40 at Junction 4 and take the A4010 following Aylesbury signs. Go straight on at 3 mini-roundabouts then bear sharp left at the 4th roundabout into Lane End Road. Fork right into Hillbottom Road at the next roundabout. The ground is at the end of the road. Hillbottom Road is on the Sands Industrial Estate; From the Town Centre: Take the A40 West and after 1½ miles turn left into Chapel Lane (after the traffic lights). Turn right then right again at the mini-roundabout into Lane End Road – then as above.

F.A. Premier League 2019/2020 Season	Arsenal	Aston Villa	AFC Bournemouth	Brighton & Hove Albion	Burnley	Chelsea	Crystal Palace	Everton	Leicester City	Liverpool	Manchester City	Manchester United	Newcastle United	Norwich City	Sheffield United	Southampton	Tottenham Hotspur	Watford	West Ham United	Wolverhampton Wanderers
Arsenal		3-2	1-0	1-2	2-1	1-2	2-2	3-2	1-1	2-1	0-3	2-0	4-0	4-0	1-1	2-2	2-2	3-2	1-0	1-1
Aston Villa	1-0		1-2	2-1	2-2	1-2	2-0	2-0	1-4	1-2	1-6	0-3	2-0	1-0	0-0	1-3	2-3	2-1	0-0	0-1
Bournemouth	1-1	2-1		3-1	0-1	2-2	0-2	3-1	4-1	0-3	1-3	1-0	1-4	0-0	1-1	0-2	0-0	0-3	2-2	1-2
Brighton & Hove Albion	2-1	1-1	2-0		1-1	1-1	0-1	3-2	0-2	1-3	0-5	0-3	0-0	2-0	0-1	0-2	3-0	1-1	1-1	2-2
Burnley	0-0	1-2	3-0	1-2		2-4	0-2	1-0	2-1	0-3	1-4	0-2	1-0	2-0	1-1	3-0	1-1	1-0	3-0	1-1
Chelsea	2-2	2-1	0-1	2-0	3-0		2-0	4-0	1-1	1-2	2-1	0-2	1-0	1-0	2-2	0-2	2-1	3-0	0-1	2-0
Crystal Palace	1-1	1-0	1-0	1-1	0-1	2-3		0-0	0-2	1-2	0-2	0-2	1-0	2-0	0-1	0-2	1-1	1-0	2-1	1-1
Everton	0-0	1-1	1-3	1-0	1-0	3-1	3-1		2-1	0-0	1-3	1-1	2-2	0-2	0-2	1-1	1-1	1-0	2-0	3-2
Leicester City	2-0	4-0	3-1	0-0	2-1	2-2	3-0	2-1		0-4	0-1	0-2	5-0	1-1	2-0	1-2	2-1	2-0	4-1	0-0
Liverpool	3-1	2-0	2-1	2-1	1-1	5-3	4-0	5-2	2-1		3-1	2-0	3-1	4-1	2-0	4-0	2-1	2-0	3-2	1-0
Manchester City	3-0	3-0	2-1	4-0	5-0	2-1	2-2	2-1	3-1	4-0		1-2	5-0	5-0	2-0	2-1	2-2	8-0	2-0	0-2
Manchester United	1-1	2-2	5-2	3-1	0-2	4-0	1-2	1-1	1-0	1-1	2-0		4-1	4-0	3-0	2-2	2-1	3-0	1-1	0-0
Newcastle United	0-1	1-1	2-1	0-0	0-0	1-0	1-0	1-2	0-3	1-3	2-2	1-0		0-0	3-0	2-1	1-3	1-1	2-2	1-1
Norwich City	2-2	1-5	1-0	0-1	0-2	2-3	1-1	0-1	1-0	0-1	3-2	1-3	3-1		1-2	0-3	2-2	0-2	0-4	1-2
Sheffield United	1-0	2-0	2-1	1-1	3-0	3-0	1-0	0-1	1-2	0-1	0-1	3-3	0-2	1-0		0-1	3-1	1-1	1-0	1-0
Southampton	0-2	2-0	1-3	1-1	1-2	1-4	1-1	1-2	0-9	1-2	1-0	1-1	0-1	2-1	3-1		1-0	2-1	0-1	2-3
Tottenham Hotspur	2-1	3-1	3-2	2-1	5-0	0-2	4-0	1-0	3-0	0-1	2-0	1-1	0-1	2-1	1-1	2-1		1-1	2-0	2-3
Watford	2-2	3-0	0-0	0-3	0-3	1-2	0-0	2-3	1-1	3-0	0-4	2-0	2-1	2-1	0-0	1-3	0-0		1-3	2-1
West Ham United	1-3	1-1	4-0	3-3	0-1	3-2	1-2	1-1	1-2	0-2	0-5	2-0	2-3	2-0	1-1	3-1	2-3	3-1		0-2
Wolverhampton Wanderers	0-2	2-1	1-0	0-0	1-1	2-5	2-0	3-0	0-0	1-2	3-2	1-1	1-1	3-0	1-1	1-1	1-2	2-0	2-0	

EFL Championship 2019/2020 Season	Barnsley	Birmingham City	Blackburn Rovers	Brentford	Bristol City	Cardiff City	Charlton Athletic	Derby County	Fulham	Huddersfield Town	Hull City	Leeds United	Luton Town	Middlesbrough	Millwall	Nottingham Forest	Preston North End	Queen's Park Rangers	Reading	Sheffield Wednesday	Stoke City	Swansea City	West Bromwich Albion	Wigan Athletic
Barnsley	■	0-1	2-0	1-3	2-2	0-2	2-2	2-2	1-0	2-1	3-1	0-2	1-3	1-0	0-0	1-0	0-3	5-3	1-1	1-1	2-4	1-1	1-1	0-0
Birmingham City	2-0	■	1-0	1-1	1-1	1-1	1-1	1-3	0-1	0-3	3-3	4-5	2-1	2-1	1-1	2-1	0-1	0-2	1-3	3-3	2-1	1-3	2-3	2-3
Blackburn Rovers	3-2	1-1	■	1-0	3-1	0-0	1-2	1-0	0-1	2-2	3-0	1-3	1-2	1-0	2-0	1-1	1-1	2-1	4-3	2-1	0-0	2-2	1-1	0-0
Brentford	1-2	0-1	2-2	■	1-1	2-1	2-1	3-0	1-0	0-1	1-1	1-1	7-0	3-2	3-2	0-1	1-0	3-1	1-0	5-0	0-0	3-1	1-0	3-0
Bristol City	1-0	1-3	0-2	0-4	■	0-1	2-1	3-2	1-1	5-2	2-1	1-3	3-0	2-2	1-2	0-0	1-1	2-0	1-0	1-2	1-1	0-0	0-3	2-2
Cardiff City	3-2	4-2	2-3	2-2	0-1	■	0-0	2-1	1-1	2-1	3-0	2-0	2-1	1-0	1-1	0-1	0-0	3-0	1-1	1-1	1-0	0-0	2-1	2-2
Charlton Athletic	2-1	0-1	0-2	1-0	3-2	2-2	■	3-0	0-0	0-1	2-2	1-0	3-1	0-1	0-1	1-1	1-0	1-0	0-1	1-3	3-1	1-2	2-2	2-2
Derby County	2-1	3-2	3-0	1-3	1-2	1-1	2-1	■	1-1	1-1	1-0	1-3	2-0	2-0	0-1	1-1	1-0	1-1	2-1	1-1	4-0	0-0	1-1	1-0
Fulham	0-3	1-0	2-0	0-2	1-2	2-0	2-2	3-0	■	3-2	0-3	2-1	3-2	1-0	4-0	1-2	2-0	2-1	1-2	5-3	1-0	1-0	1-1	2-0
Huddersfield Town	2-1	1-1	2-1	0-0	2-1	0-3	4-0	1-2	1-2	■	3-0	0-2	0-2	0-0	1-1	2-1	0-0	2-0	0-2	0-2	2-5	1-1	2-1	0-2
Hull City	0-1	3-0	0-1	1-5	1-3	2-2	0-1	2-0	0-1	1-2	■	0-4	0-1	2-1	0-1	0-2	4-0	2-3	2-1	1-0	2-1	4-4	0-1	2-2
Leeds United	1-0	1-0	2-1	1-0	1-0	3-3	4-0	1-1	3-0	2-0	2-0	■	1-1	4-0	3-2	1-1	1-1	2-0	1-0	0-2	5-0	0-1	1-0	0-1
Luton Town	1-1	1-2	3-2	2-1	3-0	0-1	2-1	3-2	3-3	2-1	0-3	1-2	■	3-3	1-1	1-2	1-1	1-1	0-5	1-0	1-1	0-1	1-2	2-1
Middlesbrough	1-0	1-1	1-1	1-1	1-3	1-3	1-0	2-2	0-0	1-0	2-2	0-1	0-1	■	1-1	2-2	1-1	1-0	1-0	1-4	2-1	0-3	0-1	1-0
Millwall	1-2	0-0	1-0	1-0	1-1	2-2	2-1	2-3	1-1	4-1	1-1	2-1	3-1	0-2	■	2-2	1-0	1-2	2-0	1-0	2-0	1-1	0-2	2-2
Nottingham Forest	1-0	3-0	3-2	1-0	1-0	0-1	0-1	1-0	0-1	3-1	1-2	2-0	3-1	1-1	0-3	■	1-1	0-0	1-1	0-4	1-4	2-2	1-2	1-0
Preston North End	5-1	2-0	3-2	2-0	3-3	1-3	2-1	0-1	2-1	3-1	2-1	1-1	2-1	0-2	0-1	1-1	■	1-3	0-2	2-1	3-1	1-1	0-1	3-0
Queens Park Rangers	0-1	2-2	4-2	1-3	0-1	6-1	2-2	2-1	1-2	1-1	1-2	1-0	3-2	2-2	4-3	0-4	2-0	■	2-2	0-3	4-2	1-3	0-2	3-1
Reading	2-0	2-3	1-2	0-3	0-1	3-0	0-2	3-0	1-4	0-0	1-1	0-1	3-0	1-2	2-1	1-1	1-0	1-0	■	1-3	1-1	1-4	1-2	0-3
Sheffield Wednesday	2-0	1-1	0-5	2-1	1-0	1-2	1-0	1-3	1-1	0-0	0-1	0-0	1-0	0-0	1-1	1-3	1-2	0-3	0-3	■	1-0	2-2	0-3	1-0
Stoke City	4-0	2-0	1-2	1-0	1-2	2-0	3-1	2-2	2-0	5-1	0-3	3-0	0-2	0-0	2-3	0-2	1-2	0-0	0-0	3-2	■	2-0	0-2	2-1
Swansea City	0-0	3-0	1-1	0-3	1-0	1-0	1-0	2-3	1-2	3-1	2-1	0-1	0-1	3-1	0-1	0-1	3-2	0-0	1-1	2-1	1-2	■	0-0	2-1
West Bromwich Albion	2-2	0-0	3-2	1-1	4-1	4-2	2-2	2-0	0-0	4-2	4-2	1-1	2-0	0-2	1-1	2-2	2-0	2-2	1-1	2-1	0-1	5-1	■	0-1
Wigan Athletic	0-0	1-0	2-0	0-3	0-2	3-2	2-0	1-1	1-1	1-1	8-0	0-2	0-0	2-2	1-0	1-0	1-2	1-0	1-3	2-1	3-0	1-2	1-1	■

EFL League One 2019/2020 Season	Accrington Stanley	AFC Wimbledon	Blackpool	Bolton Wanderers	Bristol Rovers	Burton Albion	Coventry City	Doncaster Rovers	Fleetwood Town	Gillingham	Ipswich Town	Lincoln City	Milton Keynes Dons	Oxford United	Peterborough United	Portsmouth	Rochdale	Rotherham United	Shrewsbury Town	Southend United	Sunderland	Tranmere Rovers	Wycombe Wanderers
Accrington Stanley	■	2-1	1-1	7-1	2-1	2-0		4-0	0-1	0-1	2-0	4-3	2-1	2-2	0-2	4-1	1-2	1-2	2-3	1-2	1-3	1-2	2-3
AFC Wimbledon	1-1	■	0-0	0-0	1-3	2-2		2-1	1-2	1-0	0-0	1-1	a	1-2	1-0	1-0	3-2	1-2	1-1	1-1			0-0
Blackpool	0-1	2-0	■	2-1	2-0			3-1	2-3	2-1	2-1	0-3	2-1	4-3	1-1		1-2	0-1	2-1		1-2	1-1	
Bolton Wanderers	0-0	2-2	0-0	■	1-1	3-4	0-0		2-1		0-5		1-0	0-0		0-1	1-3		1-1	3-2	1-1	2-0	0-2
Bristol Rovers	3-3	1-2	2-1	0-2	■		1-2	0-2	0-0	1-1		1-0	3-1	0-0	2-2		1-0	0-1	4-2	2-0	2-0	0-0	
Burton Albion	1-1	1-0	0-0	2-2	2-0	■	0-0		1-0	0-0	0-1	0-2	1-0	2-2	1-1		3-1	0-1		1-1		4-2	
Coventry City	0-0	2-1	3-2	2-1	2-0		■	1-1	2-1	1-0	1-1	1-0	1-1			1-0	2-1	1-1		1-0	1-0	0-1	
Doncaster Rovers	1-1		0-1	2-1	2-0	2-2	0-1	■	3-2	1-1		2-1	1-1	1-0	2-0	1-2	1-1	2-1	2-0	3-1	1-2		3-1
Fleetwood Town	2-0	2-1	0-0		0-0	4-1	0-0	2-1	■	1-1	0-1		1-0	2-1	2-1	1-0	2-1		2-2		1-1	2-1	1-1
Gillingham		1-2	2-2	5-0		1-2		2-1		■	0-1	1-0	3-1	1-1	1-2	1-1	1-0	0-3	2-0	3-1	1-0		2-0
Ipswich Town	4-1	2-1	2-2		1-2	4-1	0-1	0-0	0-1	0-0	■	1-0		0-1	1-4			0-2	3-0		1-1	4-1	0-0
Lincoln City	2-0		1-0	5-1	0-1	3-2		2-0	0-0	5-3		■	1-1	0-6	2-1	0-2		0-1	0-0	4-0	2-0	1-0	
MK Dons		2-1		1-0	3-0	0-3	0-0	0-1		0-1	2-1		■	1-0	0-4	3-1	2-1	2-3	1-0	0-1	0-1	1-3	2-0
Oxford United	3-0	5-0	2-1			2-4	3-3	3-0		3-0	0-0	1-0		■	1-0		3-0	1-3	0-0	2-1	0-1	3-0	1-0
Peterborough United	4-0	3-2		1-0		1-0	2-2	0-3	1-3	0-0	2-2	2-0		4-0	■	2-0	6-0	2-1		4-0	3-0		4-0
Portsmouth		2-1		1-0		2-2	3-3		2-2	0-0	1-0	1-0	3-1	1-1	2-2	■	3-0	3-2	2-0	4-1	2-0	2-0	2-0
Rochdale	2-1		0-0	2-0	1-2		1-2	1-1	2-3	2-2	0-1	1-1	2-0			0-3	■	3-1	1-0		1-2		0-3
Rotherham United	1-0	2-2	2-1	6-1	3-0	3-2	4-0		2-2		1-0	0-2	1-1	1-2	4-0		0-1	■	0-0			1-1	0-1
Shrewsbury Town	0-2			3-4	0-0	2-1	1-0	0-3	1-1		1-1	1-1	2-3	1-0	1-0	0-0	1-2		■	4-3	1-0	2-3	
Southend United	0-1	1-4	1-3		3-1	2-3	0-2	1-7	3-3	0-1	1-3	2-1	2-2	0-4	0-2		0-3	2-2		■		1-0	0-0
Sunderland		3-1	1-1	0-0	3-0	1-2	1-1	0-0	1-1	2-2	1-0	3-1	2-1	1-1		2-1	3-0	1-1		1-0	■	5-0	4-0
Tranmere Rovers	1-1	1-0	1-1	5-0	0-0	2-1	1-4	0-3		2-2	1-2			2-2	0-2	2-3		0-1	1-1	0-1		■	0-2
Wycombe Wanderers	1-1		2-1	2-0	3-1	2-0	1-4	1-0	0-1		1-1	3-1	3-2		3-3	1-0	2-1		1-0	4-3	1-0	3-1	■

EFL League Two 2019/2020 Season	Bradford City	Cambridge United	Carlisle United	Cheltenham Town	Colchester United	Crawley Town	Crewe Alexandra	Exeter City	Forest Green Rovers	Grimsby Town	Leyton Orient	Macclesfield Town	Mansfield Town	Morecambe	Newport County	Northampton Town	Oldham Athletic	Plymouth Argyle	Port Vale	Salford City	Scunthorpe United	Stevenage	Swindon Town	Walsall
Bradford City	■	0-0	3-1	1-1		2-1		2-0	0-1	1-1		2-0	1-0	1-0	2-1	3-0	2-1	1-2	1-1	2-2	3-1	2-1		
Cambridge United	2-1	■	1-2		2-1	2-1		4-0	0-1	0-0	2-3	2-2	2-3	1-0	0-0		1-2	1-0		0-4	3-2	0-4	0-1	
Carlisle United	0-0	0-0	■	0-1	0-3	2-1	2-4	1-3	0-0	0-0		2-1	0-2	2-2	2-0	0-2	1-0	0-3		2-2			1-1	2-1
Cheltenham Town	3-2	1-1	2-0	■	1-1		1-1		1-2		2-1	3-0	1-0	2-1		2-1	3-0	0-1	0-0		4-1	4-2	2-2	3-1
Colchester United	0-0	1-2	3-0	0-2	■	1-1		2-2		2-3	2-1	2-1		0-1	3-1	1-0		3-0	1-1	1-0		3-1	3-1	0-0
Crawley Town	2-1		0-0	1-0	2-1	■	1-2	0-1	1-1	3-2			1-0	1-1		4-0	3-0	2-2	0-0	2-0	3-1	2-0	0-4	2-3
Crewe Alexandra	2-1	2-3	4-1	1-0	0-0	2-1	■	1-1			2-0	2-0	1-1	5-0		2-1	0-3	0-1	4-1	3-1	3-1	3-1	1-0	
Exeter City		2-0		0-0	0-0	1-1	1-1	■	1-0	1-3	2-2	1-0	1-0		1-0	3-2	5-1	4-0	2-0			2-1	1-1	3-3
Forest Green Rovers			1-4		1-0	3-1	0-0	0-1	■	1-0		1-0	2-2		0-2		1-0	0-1	2-3	1-2	0-2	0-0	2-2	1-2
Grimsby Town	1-1			0-0	2-2	1-1	0-2	0-1	2-2	■	0-4	1-0	0-1	2-1	4-2	0-3		5-2	1-0	0-1	3-1	0-3		
Leyton Orient	0-0	2-1	1-1	1-0	1-3	2-3	1-2		2-4	1-1	■	1-1	2-1		2-1	1-1	2-2		3-3		0-2	0-0	1-3	3-1
Macclesfield Town	1-1	1-0		1-1	1-1	1-1	2-3	2-1	1-1	3-0		■	0-0	0-1	1-1	0-1	1-1	1-1	2-1	0-2	1-0			
Mansfield Town	3-0	0-4	2-2	0-3	2-3			3-4	0-1	2-3		■	2-2	1-0	1-1	6-1	0-1	2-2	1-2	2-0	0-0			
Morecambe	1-2	1-1	1-1	0-0	1-1		1-1	2-3	0-2	0-2	1-0	2-0	1-1	■	2-1	2-2	1-2		2-1	2-2				0-1
Newport County	2-1	0-1	1-0	1-1		1-1	1-0	1-1		1-1	1-0	2-2	1-0	■		0-1	1-0	1-0	1-2	2-1	1-1	2-0	0-0	
Northampton Town		2-0		1-1		2-2	4-1	2-0	1-0	2-0	0-1	1-2	1-2	4-1	2-0	■	3-1	0-1	2-0	3-0	1-0	0-1	0-1	
Oldham Athletic	3-0		1-1	1-1	0-1	2-1	1-2	0-0	1-1	2-2	1-1	0-1	3-1	3-1	5-0	2-2	■		1-4	0-2				2-0
Plymouth Argyle	2-1	0-0	2-0	0-2	1-0	2-2	2-1		3-0	4-0	3-0	3-1	3-0	1-0		2-2		■	2-2	2-2	2-1	1-2	3-0	
Port Vale		1-0	2-1	1-1	3-0		3-1	2-1		1-0	2-2	2-2	3-1		1-1	0-0	1-0		■	1-1	2-2	1-1	2-0	0-1
Salford City	2-0	1-0		0-2	1-2	0-0	3-1	0-1	0-4	1-0	1-1	0-0			1-2	1-1	2-3	1-1		■	1-1	2-0	2-3	1-2
Scunthorpe United	1-1	0-2	0-1	1-0	2-2	2-2	2-2	3-1	1-0	0-2			3-0	1-2	3-0	2-2	1-3	2-1			■	0-0	0-2	0-2
Stevenage	0-1	1-1	2-3		0-0	0-0	1-5	0-1	0-0	2-1	0-3	2-2		1-0		0-1	0-0	1-2	0-1	0-1		■		
Swindon Town	1-1	4-0	3-2		0-3		3-1	2-1	0-2	3-1		3-0	1-0	3-1	0-2	0-1	2-0	1-1	3-0		2-0	1-0	■	2-1
Walsall	0-1	2-1	1-2	1-2		2-1	1-2	3-1	1-1	1-3	1-0	1-1	1-2	0-2	0-0	3-2			2-2	0-3	1-0	0-0		■

F.A. Premier League

Season 2019/2020

Liverpool	38	32	3	3	85	33	99
Manchester City	38	26	3	9	102	35	81
Manchester United	38	18	12	8	66	36	66
Chelsea	38	20	6	12	69	54	66
Leicester City	38	18	8	12	67	41	62
Tottenham Hotspur	38	16	11	11	61	47	59
Wolverhampton Wanderers	38	15	14	9	51	40	59
Arsenal	38	14	14	10	56	48	56
Sheffield United	38	14	12	12	39	39	54
Burnley	38	15	9	14	43	50	54
Southampton	38	15	7	16	51	60	52
Everton	38	13	10	15	44	56	49
Newcastle United	38	11	11	16	38	58	44
Crystal Palace	38	11	10	17	31	50	43
Brighton & Hove Albion	38	9	14	15	39	54	41
West Ham United	38	10	9	19	49	62	39
Aston Villa	38	9	8	21	41	67	35
AFC Bournemouth	38	9	7	22	40	65	34
Watford	38	8	10	20	36	64	34
Norwich City	38	5	6	27	26	75	21

Champions: Liverpool

Relegated: AFC Bournemouth, Watford and Norwich City

EFL Championship

Season 2019/2020

Leeds United	46	28	9	9	77	35	93
West Bromwich Albion	46	22	17	7	77	45	83
Brentford	46	24	9	13	80	38	81
Fulham	46	23	12	11	64	48	81
Cardiff City	46	19	16	11	68	58	73
Swansea City	46	18	16	12	62	53	70
Nottingham Forest	46	18	16	12	58	50	70
Millwall	46	17	17	12	57	51	68
Preston North End	46	18	12	16	59	54	66
Derby County	46	17	13	16	62	64	64
Blackburn Rovers	46	17	12	17	66	63	63
Bristol City	46	17	12	17	60	65	63
Queen's Park Rangers	46	16	10	20	67	76	58
Reading	46	15	11	20	59	58	56
Stoke City	46	16	8	22	62	68	56
Sheffield Wednesday	46	15	11	20	58	66	56
Middlesbrough	46	13	14	19	48	61	53
Huddersfield Town	46	13	12	21	52	70	51
Luton Town	46	14	9	23	54	82	51
Birmingham City	46	12	14	20	54	75	50
Barnsley	46	12	13	21	49	69	49
Charlton Athletic	46	12	12	22	50	65	48
Wigan Athletic	46	15	14	17	57	56	47
Hull City	46	12	9	25	57	87	45

As a result of Wigan Athletic entering administration, the club was
subject to a 12 point deduction. In accordance with the EFL regulations,
the timing of the sanction was decided when final league placings were
determined. As the club finished outside relegation places at the end
of the season, the sanction was applied to their 2019-2020 season total
and the club were duly relegated.

Promotion Play-offs

Swansea City	1	Brentford	0
Cardiff City	0	Fulham	2

Brentford	3	Swansea City	1

Brentford won 3-2 on aggregate.

Fulham	1	Cardiff City	2

Fulham won 3-2 on aggregate.

Brentford	1	Fulham	2

Promoted: Leeds United, West Bromwich Albion and Fulham

Relegated: Charlton Athletic, Wigan Athletic and Hull City

EFL League One

Season 2019/2020

Coventry City	34	18	13	3	48	30	67	1.97
Rotherham United	35	18	8	9	61	38	62	1.77
Wycombe Wanderers	34	17	8	9	45	40	59	1.74
Oxford United	35	17	9	9	61	37	60	1.71
Portsmouth	35	17	9	9	53	36	60	1.71
Fleetwood Town	35	16	12	7	51	38	60	1.71
Peterborough United	35	17	8	10	68	40	59	1.69
Sunderland	36	16	11	9	48	32	59	1.64
Doncaster Rovers	34	15	9	10	51	33	54	1.59
Gillingham	35	12	15	8	42	34	51	1.46
Ipswich Town	36	14	10	12	46	36	52	1.44
Burton Albion	35	12	12	11	50	50	48	1.37
Blackpool	35	11	12	12	44	43	45	1.29
Bristol Rovers	35	12	9	14	38	49	45	1.29
Shrewsbury Town	34	10	11	13	31	42	41	1.21
Lincoln City	35	12	6	17	44	46	42	1.20
Accrington Stanley	35	10	10	15	47	53	40	1.14
Rochdale	34	10	6	18	39	57	36	1.06
Milton Keynes Dons	35	10	7	18	36	47	37	1.06
AFC Wimbledon	35	8	11	16	39	52	35	1.00
Tranmere Rovers	34	8	8	18	36	60	32	0.94
Southend United	35	4	7	24	39	85	19	0.54
Bolton Wanderers	34	5	11	18	27	66	14	0.41

Bolton Wanderers had 12 points deducted after entering administration.

Bury started the season with a 12 point deduction after entering insolvency and were unable to field a team for the first 5 League games of the season. The club was subsequently expelled from the EFL on 27th August 2019, having played no matches.

Promotion Play-offs

Fleetwood Town 1   Wycombe Wanderers 4
Portsmouth 1   Oxford United 1

Wycombe Wanderers 2   Fleetwood Town 2
Wycombe Wanderers won 6-3 on aggregate.
Oxford United 1   Portsmouth .... 1 (aet)
Aggregate 2-2. Oxford United won 5-4 on penalties.

Oxford United 1   Wycombe Wanderers 2

Promoted: Coventry City, Rotherham United and Wycombe Wanderers

Relegated: Tranmere Rovers, Southend United and Bolton Wanderers

EFL League Two

Season 2019/2020

Swindon Town	36	21	6	9	62	39	69	1.92
Crewe Alexandra	37	20	9	8	67	43	69	1.86
Plymouth Argyle	37	20	8	9	61	39	68	1.84
Cheltenham Town	36	17	13	6	52	27	64	1.78
Exeter City	37	18	11	8	53	43	65	1.76
Colchester United	37	15	13	9	52	37	58	1.57
Northampton Town	37	17	7	13	54	40	58	1.57
Port Vale	37	14	15	8	50	44	57	1.54
Bradford City	37	14	12	11	44	40	54	1.46
Forest Green Rovers	36	13	10	13	43	40	49	1.36
Salford City	37	13	11	13	49	46	50	1.35
Walsall	36	13	8	15	40	49	47	1.31
Crawley Town	37	11	15	11	51	47	48	1.30
Newport County	36	12	10	14	32	39	46	1.28
Grimsby Town	37	12	11	14	45	51	47	1.27
Cambridge United	37	12	9	16	40	48	45	1.22
Leyton Orient	36	10	12	14	47	55	42	1.17
Carlisle United	37	10	12	15	39	56	42	1.14
Oldham Athletic	37	9	14	14	44	57	41	1.11
Scunthorpe United	37	10	10	17	44	56	40	1.08
Mansfield Town	36	9	11	16	48	55	38	1.06
Morecambe	37	7	11	19	35	60	32	0.86
Stevenage	36	3	13	20	24	50	22	0.61
Macclesfield Town	37	7	15	15	32	47	19	0.51

Macclesfield Town had 13 points deducted with a further 4 point deduction suspended following a failure to pay their players and appear for a number of matches. The EFL appealed against the disciplinary panel's decision believing it was too lenient and, on 11th August, an arbitration panel ruled that the suspended points deduction should be applied immediately so Macclesfield Town finished bottom of the league and were relegated.
The club was subsequently wound up before the start of the following season.

Promotion Play-offs

Colchester United 1   Exeter City 0
Northampton Town 0   Cheltenham Town 2

Exeter City 3   Colchester United .... 1 (aet)
Exeter City won 3-2 on aggregate.
Cheltenham Town 0   Northampton Town 3
Northampton Town won 3-2 on aggregate.

Exeter City 0   Northampton Town 4

Promoted: Swindon Town, Crewe Alexandra, Plymouth Argyle and Northampton Town

Relegated: Macclesfield Town

F.A. Cup 2019/2020

Round 1	AFC Wimbledon	1	Doncaster Rovers	1	
Round 1	Accrington Stanley	0	Crewe Alexandra	2	
Round 1	Barnet	0	Fleetwood Town	2	
Round 1	Blackpool	4	Morecambe	1	
Round 1	Bolton Wanderers	0	Plymouth Argyle	1	
Round 1	Bristol Rovers	1	Bromley	1	
Round 1	Cambridge United	1	Exeter City	1	
Round 1	Carshalton Athletic	1	Boston United	4	
Round 1	Cheltenham Town	1	Swindon Town	1	
Round 1	Chichester City	w/o	Bury		
Round 1	Chippenham Town	0	Northampton Town	3	
Round 1	Colchester United	0	Coventry City	2	
Round 1	Crawley Town	4	Scunthorpe United	1	
Round 1	Dover Athletic	1	Southend United	0	
Round 1	Dulwich Hamlet	1	Carlisle United	4	
Round 1	Ebbsfleet United	2	Notts County	3	
Round 1	Forest Green Rovers	4	Billericay Town	0	
Round 1	Gateshead	1	Oldham Athletic	2	
Round 1	Grimsby Town	1	Newport County	1	
Round 1	Harrogate Town	1	Portsmouth	2	
Round 1	Hayes & Yeading United	0	Oxford United	2	
Round 1	Ipswich Town	1	Lincoln City	1	
Round 1	Leyton Orient	1	Maldon & Tiptree	2	
Round 1	Macclesfield Town	0	Kingstonian	4	
Round 1	Maidenhead United	1	Rotherham United	3	
Round 1	Maidstone United	1	Torquay United	0	
Round 1	Mansfield Town	1	Chorley	0	
Round 1	Milton Keynes Dons	0	Port Vale	1	
Round 1	Nantwich Town	0	AFC Fylde	1	
Round 1	Oxford City	1	Solihull Moors	5	
Round 1	Salford City	1	Burton Albion	1	
Round 1	Shrewsbury Town	1	Bradford City	1	
Round 1	Stevenage	1	Peterborough United	1	
Round 1	Stourbridge	2	Eastleigh	2	
Round 1	Sunderland	1	Gillingham	1	
Round 1	Tranmere Rovers	2	Wycombe Wanderers	2	
Round 1	Walsall	2	Darlington	2	
Round 1	Wrexham	0	Rochdale	0	
Round 1	Yeovil Town	1	Hartlepool United	4	
Round 1	York City	0	Altrincham	1	
Replay	Bradford City	0	Shrewsbury Town	1	
Replay	Bromley	0	Bristol Rovers	1	
Replay	Burton Albion	4	Salford City	1	
Replay	Darlington	0	Walsall	1	
Replay	Doncaster Rovers	2	AFC Wimbledon	0	
Replay	Eastleigh	3	Stourbridge	0	
Replay	Exeter City	1	Cambridge United	0	
Replay	Gillingham	1	Sunderland	0	(aet)
Replay	Lincoln City	0	Ipswich Town	1	
Replay	Newport County	2	Grimsby Town	0	
Replay	Peterborough United	2	Stevenage	0	
Replay	Rochdale	1	Wrexham	0	
Replay	Swindon Town	0	Cheltenham Town	1	
Replay	Wycombe Wanderers	1	Tranmere Rovers	2	(aet)

Round 2	Blackpool	3	Maidstone United	1	
Round 2	Bristol Rovers	1	Plymouth Argyle	1	
Round 2	Cheltenham Town	1	Port Vale	3	
Round 2	Coventry City	1	Ipswich Town	1	
Round 2	Crawley Town	1	Fleetwood Town	2	
Round 2	Eastleigh	1	Crewe Alexandra	1	
Round 2	Exeter City	2	Hartlepool United	2	
Round 2	Forest Green Rovers	2	Carlisle United	2	
Round 2	Gillingham	3	Doncaster Rovers	0	
Round 2	Kingstonian	0	AFC Fylde	2	
Round 2	Maldon & Tiptree	0	Newport County	1	
Round 2	Northampton Town	3	Notts County	1	
Round 2	Oldham Athletic	0	Burton Albion	1	
Round 2	Peterborough United	3	Dover Athletic	0	
Round 2	Portsmouth	2	Altrincham	1	
Round 2	Rochdale	0	Boston United	0	
Round 2	Shrewsbury Town	2	Mansfield Town	0	
Round 2	Solihull Moors	3	Rotherham United	4	
Round 2	Tranmere Rovers	5	Chichester City	1	
Round 2	Walsall	0	Oxford United	1	
Replay	Boston United	1	Rochdale	2	
Replay	Carlisle United	1	Forest Green Rovers	0	
Replay	Crewe Alexandra	3	Eastleigh	1	
Replay	Hartlepool United	1	Exeter City	0	(aet)
Replay	Ipswich Town	1	Coventry City	2	
Replay	Plymouth Argyle	0	Bristol Rovers	1	
Round 3	Arsenal	1	Leeds United	0	
Round 3	Birmingham City	2	Blackburn Rovers	1	
Round 3	Bournemouth	4	Luton Town	0	
Round 3	Brentford	1	Stoke City	0	
Round 3	Brighton & Hove Albion	0	Sheffield Wednesday	1	
Round 3	Bristol City	1	Shrewsbury Town	1	
Round 3	Bristol Rovers	2	Coventry City	2	
Round 3	Burnley	4	Peterborough United	2	
Round 3	Burton Albion	2	Northampton Town	4	
Round 3	Cardiff City	2	Carlisle United	2	
Round 3	Charlton Athletic	0	West Bromwich Albion	1	
Round 3	Chelsea	2	Nottingham Forest	0	
Round 3	Crewe Alexandra	1	Barnsley	3	
Round 3	Crystal Palace	0	Derby County	1	
Round 3	Fleetwood Town	1	Portsmouth	2	
Round 3	Fulham	2	Aston Villa	1	
Round 3	Gillingham	0	West Ham United	2	
Round 3	Leicester City	2	Wigan Athletic	0	
Round 3	Liverpool	1	Everton	0	
Round 3	Manchester City	4	Port Vale	1	
Round 3	Middlesbrough	1	Tottenham Hotspur	1	
Round 3	Millwall	3	Newport County	0	
Round 3	Oxford United	4	Hartlepool United	1	
Round 3	Preston North End	2	Norwich City	4	
Round 3	Queen's Park Rangers	5	Swansea City	1	
Round 3	Reading	2	Blackpool	2	
Round 3	Rochdale	1	Newcastle United	1	
Round 3	Rotherham United	2	Hull City	3	
Round 3	Sheffield United	2	AFC Fylde	1	

Round 3	Southampton	2	Huddersfield Town	0	
Round 3	Watford	3	Tranmere Rovers	3	
Round 3	Wolverhampton Wanderers	0	Manchester United	0	
Replay	Blackpool	0	Reading	2	
Replay	Carlisle United	3	Cardiff City	4	
Replay	Coventry City	3	Bristol Rovers	0	
Replay	Manchester United	1	Wolverhampton Wanderers	0	
Replay	Newcastle United	4	Rochdale	1	
Replay	Shrewsbury Town	1	Bristol City	0	
Replay	Tottenham Hotspur	2	Middlesbrough	1	
Replay	Tranmere Rovers	2	Watford	1	(aet)
Round 4	Bournemouth	1	Arsenal	2	
Round 4	Brentford	0	Leicester City	1	
Round 4	Burnley	1	Norwich City	2	
Round 4	Coventry City	0	Birmingham City	0	
Round 4	Hull City	1	Chelsea	2	
Round 4	Manchester City	4	Fulham	0	
Round 4	Millwall	0	Sheffield United	2	
Round 4	Newcastle United	0	Oxford United	0	
Round 4	Northampton Town	0	Derby County	0	
Round 4	Portsmouth	4	Barnsley	2	
Round 4	Queen's Park Rangers	1	Sheffield Wednesday	2	
Round 4	Reading	1	Cardiff City	1	
Round 4	Shrewsbury Town	2	Liverpool	2	
Round 4	Southampton	1	Tottenham Hotspur	1	
Round 4	Tranmere Rovers	0	Manchester United	6	
Round 4	West Ham United	0	West Bromwich Albion	1	
Replay	Birmingham City	2	Coventry City	2	(aet)
	Birmingham City won 4-1 on penalties.				
Replay	Cardiff City	3	Reading	3	(aet)
	Reading won 4-1 on penalties.				
Replay	Derby County	4	Northampton Town	2	
Replay	Liverpool	1	Shrewsbury Town	0	
Replay	Oxford United	2	Newcastle United	3	(aet)
Replay	Tottenham Hotspur	3	Southampton	2	
Round 5	Chelsea	2	Liverpool	0	
Round 5	Derby County	0	Manchester United	3	
Round 5	Leicester City	1	Birmingham City	0	
Round 5	Portsmouth	0	Arsenal	2	
Round 5	Reading	1	Sheffield United	2	(aet)
Round 5	Sheffield Wednesday	0	Manchester City	1	
Round 5	Tottenham Hotspur	1	Norwich City	1	(aet)
	Norwich City won 3-2 on penalties.				
Round 5	West Bromwich Albion	2	Newcastle United	3	
Round 6	Leicester City	0	Chelsea	1	
Round 6	Newcastle United	0	Manchester City	2	
Round 6	Norwich City	1	Manchester United	2	(aet)
Round 6	Sheffield United	1	Arsenal	2	
Semi-final	Arsenal	2	Manchester City	0	
Semi-final	Chelsea	3	Manchester United	1	
FINAL	Arsenal	2	Chelsea	1	

English Football League Cup 2019/2020

Round 1	Accrington Stanley	1	Sunderland	3
Round 1	AFC Wimbledon	2	Milton Keynes Dons	2
	Milton Keynes Dons won 4-2 on penalties.			
Round 1	Barnsley	0	Carlisle United	3
Round 1	Blackburn Rovers	3	Oldham Athletic	2
Round 1	Blackpool	2	Macclesfield Town	2
	Macclesfield Town won 4-2 on penalties.			
Round 1	Bradford City	0	Preston North End	4
Round 1	Brentford	1	Cambridge United	1
	Cambridge United won 5-4 on penalties.			
Round 1	Bristol Rovers	3	Cheltenham Town	0
Round 1	Charlton Athletic	0	Forest Green Rovers	0
	Forest Green Rovers won 5-3 on penalties.			
Round 1	Colchester United	3	Swindon Town	0
Round 1	Coventry City	4	Exeter City	1
Round 1	Gillingham	2	Newport County	2
	Newport County won 4-1 on penalties.			
Round 1	Grimsby Town	1	Doncaster Rovers	0
Round 1	Huddersfield Town	0	Lincoln City	1
Round 1	Luton Town	3	Ipswich Town	1
Round 1	Mansfield Town	2	Morecambe	2
	Morecambe won 6-5 on penalties.			
Round 1	Middlesbrough	2	Crewe Alexandra	2
	Crewe Alexandra won 4-2 on penalties.			
Round 1	Nottingham Forest	1	Fleetwood Town	0
Round 1	Oxford United	1	Peterborough United	0
Round 1	Plymouth Argyle	2	Leyton Orient	0
Round 1	Port Vale	1	Burton Albion	2
Round 1	Portsmouth	3	Birmingham City	0
Round 1	Queen's Park Rangers	3	Bristol City	3
	Queen's Park Rangers won 5-4 on penalties.			
Round 1	Rochdale	5	Bolton Wanderers	2
Round 1	Salford City	0	Leeds United	3
Round 1	Scunthorpe United	0	Derby County	1
Round 1	Sheffield Wednesday received a walkover after Bury were unable to fulfil their financial obligations.			
Round 1	Shrewsbury Town	0	Rotherham United	4
Round 1	Stevenage	1	Southend United	2
Round 1	Swansea City	3	Northampton Town	1
Round 1	Tranmere Rovers	0	Hull City	3
Round 1	Walsall	2	Crawley Town	3
Round 1	West Bromwich Albion	1	Millwall	2
Round 1	Wigan Athletic	0	Stoke City	1
Round 1	Wycombe Wanderers	1	Reading	1
	Reading won 4-2 on penalties.			
Round 2	AFC Bournemouth	0	Forest Green Rovers	0
	AFC Bournemouth won 3-0 on penalties.			
Round 2	Bristol Rovers	1	Brighton & Hove Albion	2
Round 2	Burnley	1	Sunderland	3
Round 2	Burton Albion	4	Morecambe	0
Round 2	Cardiff City	0	Luton Town	3
Round 2	Crawley Town	1	Norwich City	0

Round 2	Crewe Alexandra	1	Aston Villa	6
Round 2	Crystal Palace	0	Colchester United	0
	Colchester United won 5-4 on penalties.			
Round 2	Fulham	0	Southampton	1
Round 2	Grimsby Town	0	Macclesfield Town	0
	Grimsby Town won 5-4 on penalties.			
Round 2	Leeds United	2	Stoke City	2
	Stoke City won 5-4 on penalties.			
Round 2	Lincoln City	2	Everton	4
Round 2	Newcastle United	1	Leicester City	1
	Leicester City won 4-2 on penalties.			
Round 2	Newport County	0	West Ham United	2
Round 2	Nottingham Forest	3	Derby County	0
Round 2	Oxford United	2	Millwall	2
	Oxford United won 4-2 on penalties.			
Round 2	Plymouth Argyle	2	Reading	4
Round 2	Preston North End	2	Hull City	2
	Preston North End won 5-4 on penalties.			
Round 2	Queen's Park Rangers	0	Portsmouth	2
Round 2	Rochdale	2	Carlisle United	1
Round 2	Rotherham United	0	Sheffield Wednesday	1
Round 2	Sheffield United	2	Blackburn Rovers	1
Round 2	Southend United	1	Milton Keynes Dons	4
Round 2	Swansea City	6	Cambridge United	0
Round 2	Watford	3	Coventry City	0
Round 3	Arsenal	5	Nottingham Forest	0
Round 3	Colchester United	0	Tottenham Hotspur	0
	Colchester United won 4-3 on penalties.			
Round 3	Crawley Town	1	Stoke City	1
	Crawley Town won 5-3 on penalties.			
Round 3	Luton Town	0	Leicester City	4
Round 3	Portsmouth	0	Southampton	4
Round 3	Preston North End	0	Manchester City	3
Round 3	Sheffield Wednesday	0	Everton	2
Round 3	Watford	2	Swansea City	1
Round 3	Brighton & Hove Albion	1	Aston Villa	3
Round 3	Burton Albion	2	Bournemouth	0
Round 3	Chelsea	7	Grimsby Town	1
Round 3	Manchester United	1	Rochdale	1
	Manchester United won 5-3 on penalties.			
Round 3	Milton Keynes Dons	0	Liverpool	2
Round 3	Oxford United	4	West Ham United	0
Round 3	Sheffield United	0	Sunderland	1
Round 3	Wolverhampton Wanderers	1	Reading	1
	Wolverhampton Wanderers won 4-2 on penalties.			
Round 4	Everton	2	Watford	0
Round 4	Manchester City	3	Southampton	1
Round 4	Crawley Town	1	Colchester United	3
Round 4	Oxford United	1	Sunderland	1
Round 4	Aston Villa	2	Wolverhampton Wanderers	1
Round 4	Burton Albion	1	Leicester City	3
Round 4	Chelsea	1	Manchester United	2
Round 4	Liverpool	5	Arsenal	5
	Liverpool won 5-4 on penalties.			

Round 5	Oxford United	1	Manchester City	3
Round 5	Manchester United	3	Colchester United	0
Round 5	Aston Villa	5	Liverpool	0
Round 5	Everton	2	Leicester City	2
	Leicester City won 4-2 on penalties.			
Semi-finals				
1st leg	Manchester United	1	Manchester City	3
1st leg	Leicester City	1	Aston Villa	1
2nd leg	Manchester City	0	Manchester United	1
	Manchester City won 3-2 on aggregate.			
2nd leg	Aston Villa	2	Leicester City	1
	Aston Villa won 3-2 on aggregate.			
FINAL	Manchester City	2	Aston Villa	1

Cup Statistics courtesy of www.soccerdata.com

ENGLAND INTERNATIONAL LINE-UPS AND STATISTICS 2019

22nd March 2019
v CZECH REPUBLIC (ECQ)   *Wembley*

J. Pickford	Everton
K. Walker	Manchester City
M. Keane	Everton
H. Maguire	Leicester City
B. Chilwell	Leicester City
J. Henderson	Liverpool
E. Dier	Tott. Hotspur (sub. R. Barkley 17)
D. Alli	Tottenham Hotspur (sub. D. Rice 63)
J. Sancho	Borussia Dortmund
H. Kane	Tottenham Hotspur
R. Sterling	Man. City (sub. C. Hudson-Odoi 70)

Result 5-0   Sterling 3, Kane (pen), Kalas (og)

25th March 2019
v MONTENEGRO (ECQ) *Podgorica*

J. Pickford	Everton
K. Walker	Manchester City
M. Keane	Everton
H. Maguire	Leicester City
D. Rose	Tottenham Hotspur
R. Barkley	Chelsea (sub. J. Ward-Prowse 82)
D. Rice	West Ham United
D. Alli	Tott. Hotspur (sub. J. Henderson 64)
C. Hudson-Odoi	Chelsea
H. Kane	Tott. Hotspur (sub. C. Wilson 83)
R. Sterling	Manchester City

Result 5-1   Keane, Barkley 2, Kane, Sterling

6th June 2019
v NETHERLANDS (NL)   *Guimaraes*

J. Pickford	Everton
K. Walker	Manchester City
J. Stones	Manchester City
H. Maguire	Leicester City
B. Chilwell	Leicester City
F. Delph	Man. City (sub. J. Henderson 77)
D. Rice	West Ham United (sub. D. Alli 105)
R. Barkley	Chelsea
R. Sterling	Manchester City
M. Rashford	Manchester United (sub. H. Kane 45)
J. Sancho	Bor. Dortmund (sub. J. Lingard 61)

Result 1-3 (aet)   Rashford (pen)

9th June 2019
v SWIZERLAND (NL)   *Guimaraes*

J. Pickford	Everton
T. Alexander-Arnold	Liverpool
J. Gomez	Liverpool
H. Maguire	Leicester City
D. Rose	Tott. Hotspur (sub. K. Walker 70)
J. Lingard	Man. United (sub. J. Sancho 105)
E. Dier	Tottenham Hotspur
F. Delph	Man. City (sub. R. Barkley 105)
D. Alli	Tottenham Hotspur
R. Sterling	Manchester City
H. Kane	Tott. Hotspur (sub. C. Wilson 75)

Result 0-0 (aet)
England won 6-5 on penalties

7th September 2019
v BULGARIA (ECQ)   *Wembley*

J. Pickford	Everton)
K. Trippier	Atletico Madrid
M. Keane	Everton
H. Maguire	Manchester United
D. Rose	Tottenham Hotspur
J. Henderson	Liverpool (sub. M. Mount 67)
D. Rice	West Ham United
R. Barkley	Chelsea
M. Rashford	Manchester United
H. Kane	Tottenham Hotspur
	(sub. A. Oxlade-Chamberlain 77)
R. Sterling	Manchester City (sub. J. Sancho 71)

Result 4-0   Kane 3 (2 pens), Sterling

10th September 2019
v KOSOVO (ECQ)   *Wembley*

J. Pickford	Everton
T. Alexander-Arnold	Liverpool
B. Chilwell	Chelsea
D. Rice	West Ham United
M. Keane	Everton
H. Maguire	Manchester United
R. Sterling	Manchester City
J. Henderson	Liverpool
H. Kane	Tottenham Hotspur
R. Barkley	Chelsea (sub. M. Mount 83)
J. Sancho	Bor. Dortmund (sub. M. Rashford 85)

Result 5-3   Sterling, Kane, Vojvoda (og), Sancho 2

ENGLAND INTERNATIONAL LINE-UPS AND STATISTICS 2019-2020

11th October 2019
v CZECH REPUBLIC (ECQ)   *Prague*

J. Pickford	Everton
K. Trippier	Athletico Madrid
D. Rose	Tottenham Hotspur
M. Keane	Everton
H. Maguire	Manchester United
J. Henderson	Liverpool
D. Rice	West Ham Utd (sub. T. Abraham 88)
J. Sancho	Bor. Dortmund (sub. M. Rashford 73)
M. Mount	Chelsea (sub. R. Barkley 72)
R. Sterling	Manchester City
H. Kane	Tottenham Hotspur

Result 1-2   Kane (pen)

14th October 2019
v BULGARIA (ECQ)   *Sofia*

J. Pickford	Everton
K. Trippier	Athletico Madrid
H. Maguire	Manchester United
T. Mings	Aston Villa
B. Chilwell	Chelsea
J. Henderson	Liverpool
H. Winks	Tottenham Hotspur
R. Barkley	Chelsea (sub. M. Mount 73)
R. Sterling	Manchester City (sub. J. Sancho 73)
H. Kane	Tottenham Hotspur
M. Rashford	Manchester Utd (sub. C. Wilson 76)

Result 6-0   Rashford, Barkley 2, Sterling 2, Kane

14th November 2019
v MONTENEGRO (ECQ) *Wembley*

J. Pickford	Everton
T. Alexander-Arnold	Liverpool
B. Chilwell	Chelsea
H. Winks	Tottenham Hotspur
J. Stones	Manchester City
H. Maguire	Leicester City
J. Sancho	Borussia Dortmund
A. Oxlade-Chamberlain	Liverpool (sub. J. Maddison 56)
H. Kane	Tottenham H. (sub. T. Abraham 57)
M. Mount	Chelsea (sub. J. Gomez 70)
M. Rashford	Manchester United

Result 7-0   Oxlade-Chamberlain, Kane 3, Rashford, Sofranac (og), Abraham

17th November 2019
v KOSOVO (ECQ)   *Pristina*

N. Pope	Burnley
T. Alexander-Arnold	Liverpool (sub. F. Tomori 84)
B. Chilwell	Chelsea
D. Rice	West Ham United
H. Maguire	Manchester City
T. Mings	Aston Villa
R. Sterling	Manchester City
A. Oxlade-Chamberlain	Liverpool (sub. M. Mount 73)
H. Kane	Tottenham Hotspur
H. Winks	Tottenham Hotspur
C. Hudson-Odoi	Chelsea (sub. M. Rashford 59)

Result 4-0   Winks, Kane, Rashford, Mount

5th September 2020
v ICELAND (NL)   *Reykjavik*

J. Pickford	Everton
K. Walker	Manchester City
K. Tripper	Atlético Madrid
D. Rice	West Ham United
J. Gomez	Liverpool
E. Dier	Tottenham Hotspur
R. Sterling	Manchester City
J. Ward-Prowse	Southampton
J. Sancho	Borussia Dortmund (sub. T. Alexander-Arnold 73)
H. Kane	Tottenham (sub. M. Greenwood 78)
P. Foden	Manchester City (sub. D. Ings 68)

Result 1-0   Sterling (pen)

8th September 2020
vs DENMARK (NL)   *Reykjavik*

J. Pickford	Everton
T. Alexander-Arnold	Liverpool (sub. A. Maitland-Niles 86)
K. Trippier	Atlético Madrid
C. Coady	Wolverhampton Wanderers
J. Gomez	Liverpool
E. Dier	Tottenham Hotspur
K. Phillips	Leeds United (sub. J. Grealish 76)
D. Rice	West Ham United
H. Kane	Tottenham Hotspur
R. Sterling	Manchester City
J. Sancho	Bor. Dortmund (sub. M. Mount 70)

Result 0-0

Supporters' Guides and Tables books

Our Supporters' Guide series has been published since 1982 and the new 2021 editions contain the 2019/2020 Season's results and tables, Directions, Photographs, Telephone numbers, Parking information, Admission details, Disabled information and much more.

Our Football Tables books are perfect companions to the Supporters' Guides and contain historical Football League, Non-League and Scottish final tables up to the end of the 2019/2020 season.

THE SUPPORTERS' GUIDE TO PREMIER & FOOTBALL LEAGUE CLUBS 2021

This 37th edition covers all 92 Premiership and Football League clubs. *Price £9.99*

NON-LEAGUE SUPPORTERS' GUIDE AND YEARBOOK 2021

This 29th edition covers all 67 clubs in Step 1 & Step 2 of Non-League football – the Vanarama National League, National League North and National League South. *Price £9.99*

SCOTTISH FOOTBALL SUPPORTERS' GUIDE AND YEARBOOK 2021

The 28th edition features all Scottish Professional Football League, Highland League and Lowland League clubs. *Price £9.99*

ENGLISH FOOTBALL LEAGUE & F.A. PREMIER LEAGUE TABLES 1888-2020

The 23rd edition contains every Football League & F.A. Premier League final table plus play-off results and F.A. Cup and League Cup semi-final & final results. *Price £9.99*

NON-LEAGUE FOOTBALL TABLES 1889-2020

The 19th edition contains final league tables and historical notes for the 3 Leagues operating at Steps 3 and 4 of the pyramid, the Northern Premier League, Southern League and Isthmian League. This edition also covers the Staffordshire County Senior League 2005-2020. *Price £9.99*

SCOTTISH FOOTBALL TABLES 1890-2020

The 10th edition contains final league tables for all Scottish Professional Football League, Scottish League, Scottish Premier League, Highland League and Lowland Football League seasons plus the East of Scotland Football League. *Price £9.99*

These books are available UK & Surface post free from –

Soccer Books Limited (Dept. SBL)
72 St. Peter's Avenue
Cleethorpes, DN35 8HU
United Kingdom